THE ROBOT REVOLUTION

by
Tom Logsdon

ILLUSTRATED BY ED ROMAN

COMPUTER BOOK DIVISION
SIMON & SCHUSTER, INC.
New York

Published by the Computer Book Division
Simon & Schuster, Inc.
Simon & Schuster Building
Rockefeller Center
1230 Avenue of the Americas
New York, New York 10020
SIMON AND SCHUSTER and colophon are registered trademarks
of Simon & Schuster, Inc.
Designed by Irving Perkins Associates
Manufactured in the United States of America

1   2   3   4   5   6   7   8   9   10

Library of Congress Cataloging in Publication Data
Logsdon, Tom, (date)
   The robot revolution.

   1.Robotics 2.Robots, Industrial. I.Title.
TJ211.L63   1984   629.8′92   84-1275
ISBN 0-671-46705-0 Pbk.

Acknowledgments

This book has been a cooperative venture involving the efforts of many individuals who deserve special recognition. In particular, I would like to single out Thomas Carroll, who furnished most of the material in Chapters 8 and 9. For years Carroll has been building and designing robots for various applications, even for repairing and servicing satellites in space. A prolific writer, his most recent articles, in *Popular Mechanics*, describe the construction and use of home and hobby robots. His assistance, counsel, and writing abilities are greatly appreciated.

I would also like to thank Edward Roman, who drew most of the illustrations. Working with Ed is always a pleasant and rewarding enterprise. Special thanks go also to Elda Stramel, who typed all the rough drafts and the final manuscript with professional ease—even when impossible deadlines began to loom on the horizon. The efforts of Melodie Earickson, who helped in proofing the galleys and index, are also greatly appreciated. Finally, I would like to give special thanks to my daughter, Donna Logsdon, who helped me throughout the project with morale building, fact checking, and research.

me throughout the project with morale building, fact checking, and research.

A number of other individuals served as interview sources and/or showed me the inner workings of their favorite robots. Most particularly I would like to thank:

- Joel Slutzky, Chairman of the Board of Odetics, Inc., in Anaheim, California, developers of the "Functionoid," a six-legged robot with impressive strength and versatility.
- David Coleman of the Robot Factory in Cascade, Colorado, developer of a family of ice-skating robots with names like "Bagley T. Brat" and "Commander I."
- Dr. Hans Berliner at Pittsburgh's Carnegie-Mellon University, who masterminded the "Gammonoid" robot that successfully defeated the world-champion backgammon player.
- Dr. Earl Sacerdoti and Dr. David L. Milgram of Machine Intelligence in Mountain View, California, who helped me understand their special techniques for teaching machines to "see and think."
- G. W. "Dusty" Rhodes of Microbot Corporation, developers of the Teachmover, a cleverly designed educational robot used in classroom demonstrations.
- John Purbrick of the M.I.T. Robotics Laboratory, who has done some impressive research in attempting to construct "artificial skin" to give robots the sense of touch.
- Dr. Joseph Weitzenbaum, also of M.I.T., who has written unusually lucid accounts of the rampant computerization of our society.
- Donald L. Stansbarger, a helpful and enthusiastic interview source at Northrop Corporation in Hawthorne, California, where robots are being used in the making of high-performance military aircraft.
- Ray Bradbury, science-fiction writer, who provided me with some useful insights into the social implications of robots.
- Jack Boddy, computer expert at the Space Division of Rockwell International, who took me on an electronic guided tour of his company's CAD/CAM systems.
- Dr. Jerry Saveriano, lecturer on robotics, who generously furnished me with key industry statistics.
- Carl R. Witham, who showed me around Unimation's fascinating research laboratories in Silicon Valley.

- Ms. B. J. Snyder, who described the inner workings of a skillful little robot that cleans gyroscopes for a living at Autonetics in Anaheim, California.
- Gary R. Martins of Intelligent Software, who skillfully summarized for me and my classmates, the recent breakthroughs in artificial intelligence.
- Nan Paik, a professional librarian, who helped me ferret out a number of obscure sources and helpful statistics.
- Robert C. Eckhardt and Robert Gehorsam, my editors at Simon and Schuster, who guided this project to completion with impeccable craftsmanship.

Without the kind assistance of these many helpful people, this book would not have been nearly as comprehensive, nor nearly as much fun to write.

Tom Logsdon
Seal Beach, California
1984

This book is dedicated to "Prof." Robert Robertson and Dr. Smith Park, who many years ago helped a brash young student stay in school.

Contents

1. Introduction 11
2. What Is a Robot? 18
3. Robots in History 33
4. Machines That See and Feel 56
5. Machines "Who" Think? 78
6. The Factory of the Future 97
7. Robots and Military Power 113
8. Show Robots 133
9. How to Build Your Own Robot 150
10. Robots for the Future 169
    Appendix 191

CHAPTER 1

INTRODUCTION

It sits all alone at the foot of Mount Fuji huddled among the pine trees of rural Japan. Tourists hardly ever notice it at all. But it is a factory unlike any other anywhere in the world. For one thing, it contains long rows of birdlike industrial robots. Of course, these days that's not particularly unusual; at this moment more than 15,000 robots are working in Japan, the biggest robot power on earth. What is so unusual about this specific factory is the product its robots are trained to make. Working tirelessly day and night, they make other robots.

A work force of only 60 robots produces 100 duplicates every month. A few dozen human workers help out during the day, but when they return home at night, the factory continues to hum with the sounds of an unending mechanical dance, executed almost entirely without human intervention. Everything is automated, including the fleets of driverless trucks that zip across the factory floor bringing new parts to the robots and taking away finished subassemblies. At night the robots work in subdued light. They could work in the dark—they're blind; but their human supervisors would be unable to spot robot tangles and other problems on the factory floor. Safety precautions here, as in other robot assembly lines, are minimal. An injured robot may require repairs, but it doesn't sue.

Think about that factory's work force for a minute. It consists of 60 self-replicating machines capable of doubling their number every 20 days. We human beings are also self-replicating. Depending on how you look at it, our method of replication is either much simpler—or much more complicated—than the method used by Japan's robots. But there is an important difference; instead of 20 days, it takes the people on earth about 35 years to double their number. If present trends continue, the 4 billion people living on our planet will be 8 billion by the year 2018.

Theoretically, within a single decade Japan's industrial robots could match the earth's human population, even if only 10 percent of their robot offspring were put to work making duplicate robots. Of course, for a number of reasons, things can't possibly happen that fast. Raw materials, factory space, repair capabilities, electrical power would all run out if the Japanese tried to create such a rapid expansion of the world's robot population. However, prices will inevitably plummet when robots begin replicating themselves by the tens of thousands, just as the price of transistors plummeted when they became clever enough to contribute to their own reproduction. Today's transistor-designed transistors cost only about $1/100$ as much as their manually designed counterparts did 20 years ago.

Industrial robots help us work more efficiently in a variety of ways. About 40 percent of the ones in current use have been bought by the auto industry. They huddle beside assembly lines spray-painting cars. They deftly pick up, insert, and screw in tiny dash-panel light bulbs. They assemble small components and inspect the finished product, setting aside any units that fail to meet specifications. They also handle a number of other tricky assignments, sometimes with remarkable efficiency. At Chrysler's 145-acre Jefferson plant in East Detroit, Michigan, for instance, 50 robots crank forward spitting sparks as they weld together various models of the Plymouth Reliant and the Dodge Aries. They have replaced 200 human welders. Within a year after the robots reported to work, plant output increased 20 percent compared with conventional manufacturing techniques.

This experimental PUMA robot is installing small light bulbs in the back of a Chevrolet instrument panel. The PUMA, whose movements are computer-controlled, swivels about five different axes with joints similar to the human elbow and knee. Once it has been properly programmed, it can repeat the same motions over and over again to an accuracy of a few hundredths of an inch.

At the McDonnell-Douglas factory in St. Louis, Missouri, a robot directs a sizzling laser beam to slice through sheets of graphite used in brake assemblies for military jets. It also cuts out parts for the tail sections and the wings—which are later welded together by another robot. With their new robot assistants, 2 human workers now do the jobs once performed by 30.

At Rountree Chocolates in England, special robots with two arms pick up finished pieces of chocolate with suction cups and place them in a box, two per second. They work day and night without ever hinting for a coffee break. Joseph Engelberger, president of Unimation, first and largest of the American robot makers, considers chocolate snatching an ideal job for a robot. According to his estimate, "No [human] worker has ever lasted more than two years at that job!"

At Texas Instruments in Lewisville, Texas, robots inspect light-emitting diodes used in illuminating the numbers on pocket calculators. Humans can do the job for only about 2 hours at a stretch before they feel their nerves begin to unravel. "After two hours, all the lights look alike," observed one slightly bug-eyed Texas Instruments workman. Robots, on the other hand, work happily as diode inspectors for days on end without problems. They never strike—or complain—even if they are assigned to work on all three shifts.

At General Dynamics in Forth Worth, Texas, a T-3 robot helps make the sheet-metal parts for the F-16 military aircraft. It selects the appropriate drill bits from a tool rack and makes a precise set of holes to a tolerance of $\frac{1}{200}$ of an inch or less. A human worker doing the same job can produce 6 parts per shift, 10 percent of which must be thrown out because of defects. The robot makes 24 to 30 parts per shift with virtually no rejections. General Dynamics gladly paid a little over $60,000 for the T-3 robot. Savings totaled $93,000 during its first year on the job.

Most of the robots now in use are blind—and quite stupid; but the Japanese are developing one that sorts fish according to species. Robots in the United States sort other objects: tomatoes, wrenches, ball bearings. The technicians at Unimation have been asked to design a robot to pluck chickens; and Australian researchers are busy testing another that shears sheep. The process is supposed to be painless. The first thing the robot does is temporarily stun its victim with an electric shock. Shearing the gently sloping back and sides is easy; but even after months of careful adjustment, the robot is still having "significant difficulties" finishing up the tight bends around the neck and head. Sheep ranchers and politicians in New Zealand are following these experiments with keen interest. New Zealand is inhabited by 3.2 million people and 78 million sheep.

More exotic robots with unexpected capabilities are also creeping out of the laboratories. Professors Shigeo Hirose and Yoji Umetani at the Tokyo Institute of Technology have developed a snakelike robot that crawls through pipes and other narrow openings in machinery searching for defective parts. If simple repairs, such as tightening a bolt or clearing a clogged drain, are required, the robot handles the problem on its own without human intervention. Practical uses for the "snake" will likely include engine repairs, the cleaning of hydraulic lines, and the maintenance of oil-pipeline valves.

The Japanese also use robot traffic policemen on their highways and butlerlike robot waiters to entice customers into fancy restaurants. They are working on a number of medical robots, including one with 25 fingers that examines the female breast for suspicious lumps. Each finger is rigged with a pressure-sensitive strain gauge hooked to a computer. As the fingers squeeze the breast, subtle differences in pressure allow the computer to draw a picture that shows the location of any tumors. On the average, a conventional diagnosis requires more than 200 X-rays—which can themselves cause cancer. With the aid of the 25-fingered robot, the diagnosis can be made with only 30 X-rays, and the size and location of any suspicious lumps are pinpointed with substantially greater accuracy.

The robot clanking around inside modern Japanese factories has created a minor problem which shop technicians are circumventing in a characteristically clever manner. In Japan, robots are national heroes, and flocks of curious tourists swoop down on the plants hoping to watch them in their native habitat. Most plant managers are much too polite to turn anyone away; consequently, at some factories more hours of paid labor are expended in guided tours than in any other part of the operation. The solution is obvious, at least to the Japanese. You guessed it: robot tour guides!

A modern robot is a manipulator designed to interact physically with the real world under the direction and control of an electronic "brain." As one expert put it: "A robot is the *muscles* of a computer." In order to examine the "robot revolution" in its broadest possible context, this simple, but powerful, definition will be adopted in the remainder of this book. In some cases I may even venture a little beyond its boundaries to include "electronic" muscles such as the beam of electrons that paints images on the screen of a video display terminal under direct computer control.

Although this book is entitled *The Robot Revolution*, it could, instead, be called "The Productivity Revolution," because in the main, it deals with the many ways in which robots and computers have suddenly formed a partnership to help us enhance the efficiency of our already enormously productive society. According to George C. Devol, who holds 40 of the earliest patents in robotics, "There are really three robot businesses: the *body* business, the *brain* business, and the *systems* business." In the pages to follow we will explore all three of the businesses associated with the robot revolution.

In Chapter 2, I define industrial robots from various viewpoints and examine some of the important jobs they have been assigned to handle. In the third chapter I trace the emergence of the robot concept across the pages of history, starting with ancient legend and myth and ending with present-day technology. Chapter 4 deals with special robots rigged to "see" and "touch" the world around them, and the following chapter shows how they are using their powerful new "brains" to decide how they should respond to all this sensory input. Chapters 6 and 7 explore the use of robots and their associated technologies in the factory of the future and on the military battlefield. Strictly speaking, some of the devices to be described cannot honestly be classified as robots—even by the broadest possible definition. Nevertheless, in my view, they are a part of the overall "robot revolution" that is sweeping us inexorably into the futuristic world of the 21st century.

The eighth chapter describes the antics of show robots: special remote-controlled devices—often quite human in appearance—used for promotional and advertising purposes. Although robots of this type may seem outside the mainstream of robotics research, they are often designed with exquisite skill and care. Moreover, if present trends continue for a few more years, they will probably outnumber the more familiar industrial robots now working on our assembly lines and in our factories. Chapter 9 discusses the ways in which you can become the proud owner of your own robot, either by buying it outright (a hobby robot is surprisingly inexpensive!) or by building it in your garage or basement to your own personal specifications. The final chapter advances some fanciful speculations about the future of robotics, including space-based military robots of surprisingly advanced design and clever terrestrial models that may someday affect your health, your economic well-being, and the way you choose to spend future vacations.

CHAPTER 2

WHAT IS A ROBOT?

What is a robot? And how does it differ from other automatic machines? The term itself comes from the Czech word for "forced labor," as invented by Karel Čapek, the Czechoslovakian playwright, who popularized it in his 1921 melodrama R.U.R. (Rossum's Universal Robots). The robots in Čapek's play are metal devices that look, and behave, like people. Consequently, by today's terminology we would classify them as "androids" rather than robots. R.U.R., which capitalized on the fear and mistrust many people felt for the machine age, received mixed reviews from critics, but the public liked it. It ran for 184 performances on Broadway.

In those days defining the word "robot" was relatively easy; but it is surprisingly difficult to devise a workable definition of a *modern* robot. Any proposed definition will likely *exclude* certain machines that are widely regarded as robots or *include* such nonrobot items as automatic record changers or bottle-capping machines. The Third Edition of *Webster's New International Dictionary*, for instance, defines a robot as "a machine in the form of a human being that performs the mechanical functions of a human being." However, today's robot makers are not much interested in giving their creations human forms. Many industrial robots look and act more like drunken lobsters or oversized grasshoppers than human beings.

A few years ago the members of the Robot Institute of America, a loosely organized federation of robot makers, held a special meeting for the purpose of developing a mutually acceptable definition of an industrial robot, but it turned out to be considerably harder than any of them would have suspected. "Everybody knows what a robot is," quipped one member, "but nobody seems to be able to define one." For a while the Institute operated with a tongue-in-cheek definition: "Any machine made by one of our members."

Later, they called another meeting and, after a long debate, finally settled upon a more useful definition:

> "A reprogrammable, multifunctional manipulator designed to move material, parts, tools or specialized devices, through variable programmable motions, for the performance of a variety of tasks."

The key words in their definition are "reprogrammable" and "multifunctional." By "reprogrammable" they mean that if the robot gets a new assignment, it will need new instructions, but its basic structure will not change (although, in practice, a new mechanical hand is often required). By "multifunctional" they mean that the robot can handle a variety of tasks. Thus, a modern industrial robot is the mechanical counterpart of a general-purpose digital computer in that it can tackle various problems with no major hardware modifications. Ideally, the only thing that changes when the robot is reassigned is its program of instructions. One obvious benefit of this design philosophy is that the manufacturer can mass-produce his robots without knowing specifically how each one will be used.

The best of today's robots are essentially teleoperators with microprocessors for brains. A teleoperator is a manipulator device, usually equipped with swiveling joints, controlled and watched over at a distance by a human being. Teleoperators were developed shortly after World War II for handling dangerous radioactive substances. They are still in use. The operator slips his hands into glovelike contraptions which transmit his movements to special plierlike grippers located behind a radiation-resistant wall. By watching the grippers through a narrow slit, or on a television screen, he can move, mix, and manipulate radioactive materials without suffering harm from radiation.

In a modern robot, the human operator is replaced by one or more programmable microprocessors—cornflake-sized chips of the type found in computers and pocket calculators. A microprocessor is like a railroad switching yard built on a microscopic scale. Electronic pulses are routed through tiny switches called transistors lying on the surface of the chip. A command such as "Move claw to position 26" will cause a string of electronic pulses to flow along tiny wires through thousands of transistors. The transistors translate the command into new pulses to activate and control "muscles" powering the robot's limbs.

Even in the 1950s it was clear that electronic devices, rather than the human brain, could, in theory, be used in controlling a tele-operator. But until recently, this technique was economically imprac-tical for industrial applications because electronic switches were prohibitively large and expensive. Fortunately, these switches have been shrinking in size and cost, so that today the microprocessor "brain" is often one of the smallest and least costly components of a robot. We are now mass-producing microprocessor chips with tens of thousands of transistors, each smaller than a bacterium, and each costing only a small fraction of a cent.

Commands for controlling the robot's operations are fed to its "brain" in a number of ways. In one of the most common, the operator flips a switch to convert the robot into the "teaching mode," then moves its hand through all the desired motions manually with his own hand. When another switch is activated, the robot will repeat those same motions over and over again with exacting precision. In another pro-gramming method, a portable "teachbox" is connected to the robot. When the teachbox is in place, the operator can command the robot to move its joints through the desired motions by pushing any of several buttons; usually each button controls the movements of a single swiveling joint. When the robot's hand has reached the desired point in space, the operator pushes the "memory" button and it will "re-member" where its hand is positioned. This procedure can be repeated for as many endpoints as desired. Computer programs can also be used to control the actions of a robot. The commands in the program cause the robot's "brain" to send out a series of pulses to its joints to control its movements.

Programming industrial robots is a demanding art—there is virtually no margin for error on an assembly line. Robotics designers build careful safeguards into their creations, because they know that in many cases, robots must share the workplace with frail human workers. Unfortunately, these safety features are not always fail-safe, especially when workmen are foolhardy enough to circumvent them. Recently, for instance, at a Kawasaki plant in Japan, an industrial robot crushed a workman to death. It was one of several lathe-loading robots working within a protective 5-foot chain-link fence. The workman, who was responsible for the efficient operation of the robots, decided to climb over the fence because if he entered through the gate they would automatically shut down, thus interfering with production. Unfortunately, he was impaled by one of the machines. Although they are not normally disabled or killed, most American robotics researchers proudly exhibit cuts and scars from their encounters with experimental robots.

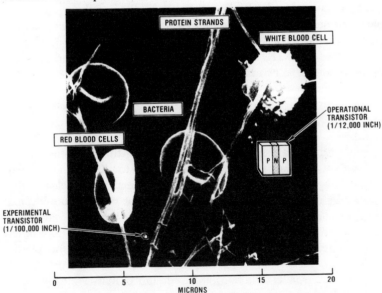

The smallest of today's transistors, which duplicate the functions of the pickle-sized vacuum tubes in old-fashioned radios, are about 2 microns wide (1/12,000 of an inch). They are smaller than white blood cells and roughly the same size as bacteria. Experimental transistors, soon to reach the marketplace, will be considerably smaller.

Most robots are equipped with a single hand (effector) and a single arm with a total of five or six articulated joints. Some of these joints swivel in smooth arcs mimicking the behavior of the human shoulder, wrist, and elbow. When we see such a robot at work, we immediately feel rapport with it, because its movements are so similar to our own. Other robots move in straight lines. Their motion is similar to that of an overhead crane running along the ceiling of a factory. The hook of the crane can be positioned over any spot on the floor by a combination of two perpendicular straight-line motions. Generally speaking, a robot that moves in this manner tends to be more precise than one with swiveling joints; however, it also occupies some of the space that might better be used by the parts being manipulated.

Rarely will a robot have a pair of arms; and when it does, they usually do not coordinate their movements; one stops while the other moves. A few are rigged with two hands. For instance, the technicians at Volkswagen have constructed a robot with two hands mounted on the two opposite ends of a long, rigid boom. It is a clever, counterbalanced design, but it takes up a great deal of space on the factory floor. For the second hand to come into use, the entire rigid arm must rotate a full 180 degrees to enable it to reach the work station. Some robots have two hands mounted side by side on the end of a single arm. It is a heavy, bulky design, but it is convenient for some applications such as inserting parts into an oven. The robot opens the oven door and removes the previously baked part with one hand, then it puts in a new part with the other hand.

Some robots have hands with two opposing thumbs; others have no hands at all. In arc welding, for instance, the torch is often mounted directly on the end of the robot's arm. Since it never releases the torch, there is no reason to equip the robot with a complicated hand or claw. Spray painting is often handled the same way. Suction cups are another common substitute for a robot hand. Among other things, they are used in picking up chocolate candies and plastic plates.

Robots are usually stationary. If they do move, that's typically about all they do. Examples are delivery robots waddling up and down the halls of office buildings delivering mail and supplies, and cartlike robots in hospitals and warehouses.

The hands and arms of early industrial robots were usually pneumatically powered (air pressure) or hydraulically powered (fluid pressure). Thus, they were more akin to steam shovels than human arms.

The power source was located in the base of the robot or some other convenient position. Flexible tubes carried pressurized gases or liquids to exert the necessary forces no matter how the robot's joints were turned. In recent years hydraulic power has held favor for heavy-lift robots, but for those that handle smaller and lighter payloads, pneumatic power has lost out to small electric motors located at the point of rotation. The arms of Unimate's PUMA (and many of its competitors) are activated in this way. Electric motors located at the point of need give a robot greater precision and control, but they slow its movements because the moving joints must constantly overcome the inertia of the heavy motors.

The human hand—the most versatile manipulator in nature—gets around this problem by using a clever approach: fibrous tendons to transmit forces around sharp corners. The result is a remarkably light and facile instrument, one whose capabilities are the envy of any robot maker. Tendon technology is used in the Teachmover robot which is produced and marketed by the Microbot Corporation in Mountain View, California. In researching this book I visited the Microbot plant, where company president G. W. "Dusty" Rhodes introduced me to his $2,000 Teachmover, a small robot which is equipped with five articulated joints similar to those in the human wrist and elbow.

The five motors driving the Teachmover's joints are all located in its base. This gives added stability. Each joint is controlled by a flexible cable running from one of the motors in the base to a pulley mounted on the joint. Springs are attached to the cables to help absorb sudden shocks, but the device still moves like an awkward adolescent going out on his first heavy date.

In a few minutes, Dusty Rhodes showed me how to operate the hand-held Teach Control used in programming the Teachmover robot. While I was waiting for my appointment, I had watched one in the lobby endlessly repeating a preprogrammed series of snakelike movements. It had looked easy then; but now that it was my turn to show off, I was beginning to feel the pressure. My assignment was to scoop up a small plastic cube from a tabletop using the robot claw. The buttons on the Teach Control activate the robot's joints one by one to swivel about any of its five axes, and a "memory" button causes it to remember the endpoints of any segment of its trajectory. It forgets everything else, including the actual path it followed in reaching the various endpoints. The motions of the Teachmover, like those of

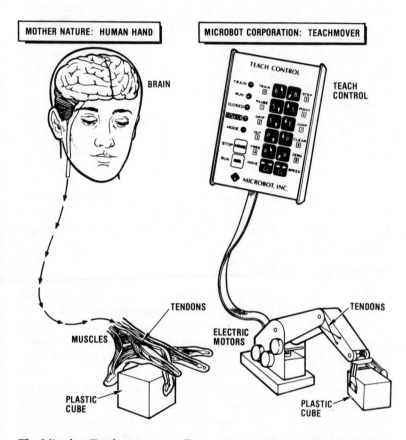

The Microbot Teachmover, a small, inexpensive instructional robot, controls its five swiveling joints with five slender tendons similar to the ones running along the fingers of the human hand. The hand-held Teach Control device is used to instruct the robot to swivel its joints in performing its assignment.

many industrial robots, are reptilian and so cute I couldn't help smiling.

When you move your own arms, your movements happen without thought, automatically; but when you are manipulating a "detached" arm, precisely controlled movements are surprisingly difficult. I finally did manage to pick up that elusive plastic cube—after an embarrassing number of abortive attempts—but not until Dusty Rhodes mercifully positioned it directly under the claw. Once I was successful, the push of another button caused the Teachmover robot to repeat its movements, picking up the cube and putting it down again and again with delightful precision.

A much more advanced robot, which also uses tendon technology, is being developed cooperatively by researchers at Stanford University and the Jet Propulsion Laboratory (JPL). When it is completed, the hand will have three fingers each rigged with three joints, just like the fingers of the human hand. With nine articulated joints it will be able to manipulate a variety of objects; and it will handle tasks impossible with the primitive pincers on most of today's robots. It may even be able to catch a small rubber ball from midair as it arcs along a parabolic trajectory.

Robots, even expensive ones, are usually blind, although, as we shall see in Chapter 4, new versions are being tested that in some respects are at least as visually sensitive to their surroundings as people. Some new models are being equipped with both vision and tactile senses (touch). In addition, some will react to stimuli that the human body cannot detect, including low-level nuclear radiation, infrared light, and ultrasound. Three-dimensional binocular vision and microscopic sight will likely be available on some advanced models.

Many low-technology robots are insensitive to their surroundings; but others have at least a crude picture of what is happening around them. The assembly lines they work on are equipped with switches, some sensitive to pressure, some triggered by beams of light, which signal the robot that a new part has arrived or that a particular operation has been completed. Robots also receive electrical impulses from electronic timers and other machines along the assembly line. If, for example, a metal part is being quenched in cold water, a timer will signal the robot when it has had enough time to cool.

Incidentally, robots have a quaint way of quenching a part. A human worker will likely use metal tongs to pick up hot parts, dropping

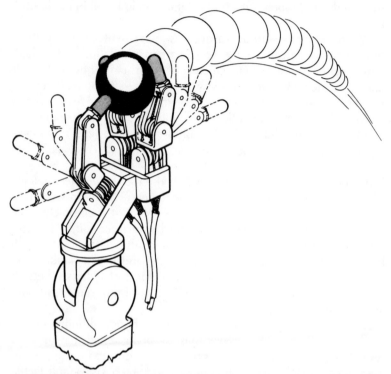

This facile three-fingered hand is being developed jointly by Stanford University and the Jet Propulsion Laboratory. In this artist's conception it is snatching a small rubber ball out of the air. It uses tendon technology similar to but much more sophisticated than that of the Microbot Teachmover.

them into the water one by one. Then, when they have all cooled, he will use the tongs to fish them out again. A robot is much more direct. It picks up a hot part in its bare metal hand, plunges both part and hand into the water, and holds them there until the part cools.

Today the Japanese are preeminent in applied robotics, and unless massive efforts are made by their competitors, they will likely remain preeminent for at least a decade. Or more. Not counting simple pick-and-place robots (which the Japanese also dominate), 60 percent of the 25,000 industrial robots currently in use around the world are working in Japan. The United States has about 5,000, and a similar number have been installed in Europe. Iron Curtain countries have only token numbers at present; however, the current 5-year plan in the Soviet Union reportedly calls for the installation of 40,000 industrial robots.

Historically, the major robot makers in the United States have been small, specialized companies, whereas Japanese robots are more typically manufactured by large conglomerates. Often Japanese companies get started by making robots for their own use, then begin selling them to other companies both domestic and foreign. International partnerships and licensing agreements are also common.

The two largest American robot makers are Unimation in Danbury, Connecticut, and Cincinnati Malicron in Ohio. Their combined market share currently exceeds 80 percent of the domestic supply. According to recent projections published in *Business Week*, if small companies such as these continue to dominate the domestic industry, sales of robots in the United States will grow to $1 billion per annum by 1990. On the other hand, if major corporations, such as IBM and General Electric, enter the marketplace in a big way, unit prices will drop, and sales can be expected to grow at a much faster rate to $2 billion per year. Under these more optimistic conditions, an annual domestic production level of 200,000 robots appears likely by 1990. Since major companies including IBM, General Electric, and others have already announced plans for marketing industrial robots, industry estimates of growth rates exceeding 35 percent per year will likely materialize.

One-third of the workers in Japan, mostly those hired by large, stable companies, have guaranteed lifetime employment. They and their countrymen love and admire robots, which are the heroes of Japanese films and comic strips. When a new robot is put on the payroll, factory workers have a celebration and give it a suitable nickname—often that of a popular baseball player or a movie star. America's workmen tend to have a more fretful attitude toward robots, although they too, on occasion, demonstrate sympathy or admiration. One such incident took place in a Cleveland, Ohio, sheet-metal stamping plant where a robot exerted Herculean efforts in an attempt to meet his production quota under the urging of his frustrated programmer. One morning, 2 months later, when the robot finally managed to reach his goal, he received a standing round of applause from every human worker in his department.

In another case in a Chicago, Illinois, automotive plant, a robot had a mechanical nervous breakdown—which must have struck a responsive chord in his fellow workers on a dirty, noisy assembly line.

At one point the robot pulled in its arm and curled into a ball, refusing to move at all. A specialist spent a week diagnosing the illness and effecting a cure. Meanwhile, the workers affectionately nicknamed the machine "Clyde the Claw." During his convalescence, the men of Production Department 14 organized a get-well party, heaping Clyde's pedestal with wild flowers and sympathy cards. The entire crew then posed with the incapacitated machine for a picture which ran in the company newspaper under the caption SICK CLYDE.

Despite their occasional playfulness, American workers, especially those in Detroit, understand that blue-collar industries are trapped in a dilemma. With increased automation, jobs will gradually disappear; without it, they may disappear even faster as auto sales shift, inexorably, toward the Land of the Rising Sun. As one auto executive put it, Detroit car factories have three choices: "automate, emigrate, or evaporate." Detroit auto worker John Hilton compares his outdated American factory with the newest robot-run auto plants in Japan:

> The Japanese are already well into a new productivity revolution, one that makes traditional factories like mine virtually obsolete. Serious automation remains largely a myth here, but in Japan, it is quickly becoming reality.... The resulting productivity... is almost unbelievable. The Zama factory [in Japan], 97 percent automated, builds cars almost without human participation, thanks to the large-scale use of programmable robots. Its daily output of 1,300 cars requires a per-shift work-force of only 67. My own plant has a comparable output—and about twenty times as many workers.

An exhaustive analysis put together by former Chrysler manufacturing executive James E. Harbour suggests that the average Japanese compact car is assembled in 14 worker-hours, as against 33 for a comparable American model. Building the Japanese engine requires 2.8 hours as against 6.8 for the U.S. engine; stamping out body parts, 2.9 hours as against 9.5. All told, the evidence indicates that the typical Japanese manufacturer builds cars with about half as many hours of labor as U.S. manufacturers. Higher pay rates and costlier fringe benefits in the United States give the Japanese an additional competitive edge in the international marketplace.

Even with today's relatively backward technology, the robot provides formidable competition for a human worker. It can work three shifts a day with no meal breaks. It doesn't call in sick from the ski slopes, never gets bored, is ineligible for vacations and pensions, and doesn't leave Coca Cola cans rattling around inside the products it is assigned to make. Because of these and other factors, the "up time" of a robot on the job averages around 95 percent, compared with 75 percent or less for the average blue-collar worker. In addition to its Horatio Alger work habits, the robot is immune to government and union regulations on heat, fumes, radiation, and other safety hazards. And it is never distracted by affections, passions, or prejudices. As one observer put it: "If you prick it, it does not bleed. If you poison it, it does not die."

But even if a robot breaks down completely, there's no call for panic. The maintenance crew merely yanks it out of the assembly line with a forklift and switches in an interchangeable replacement. In December of 1980, a *Time* magazine article reviewed the compelling economic reasons for using robots in Detroit. Here are its main conclusions:

> Two decades ago, a typical assembly-line robot cost about $25,000; that plus all operating costs over its eight-year lifetime amounted to about $4.20 per hour, slightly more than the average factory worker's wage and fringe benefits. Today the typical robot costs $40,000 . . . and it can still be paid for and operated for $4.80 an hour; the worker often costs $15 to $20. That is the formula for a gold rush.

A gold rush indeed! One prognosticator even reckons that by the turn of the century, gross revenues in the robot industry could rival those of the auto industry itself. That estimate could be optimistic, but consider what has happened in the computer industry over the past three decades. In 1950 there were only about 15 digital computers in the entire United States, and profits from their sale were virtually nonexistent. Today more than 4 million computers are in use, and the data-processing industry employs 2 million full-time workers. Revenues exceeded $55 billion in 1982.

At this moment, in a small, boxlike factory at the foot of Mount Fuji in rural Japan, swarms of industrial robots labor to make other robots. They are, for all practical purposes, self-replicating. Dr. James Albus of the U.S. National Bureau of Standards, for one, believes that such self-replicating machines will have a truly profound effect on our future. He points out that the machines working in today's factories are so outlandishly expensive because they are manufactured in small quantities—which stems in turn from the fact that they are built for narrow, specialized purposes.

By contrast, he contends that a universally programmable machine, such as a robot, produced in large quantities, could be sold for one-tenth the present price, perhaps less. But that is only the beginning of the robot revolution. He also believes that "when automatic factories begin to manufacture automatic factories, cost reductions will propagate exponentially from generation to generation." With large-scale self-replication, even the most complex computer-controlled robot might eventually cost only a few hundred noninflated dollars. Spread over a 168-hour workweek, this would yield a robot labor rate of only pennies per hour.

It may seem a little surprising that we could hire a mechanical servant to do our most distasteful work for a few cents an hour. But actually, we have all been served for decades by other machines that work for even less. Consider the refrigerator, the washing machine, the programmable pocket calculator. The only difference between these and robots is that they are special-purpose rather than general-purpose machines. Americans have difficulty realizing how completely mechanized their society actually is. Machines seem so natural to us that we barely notice them. Perhaps the best measure of mechanical efficiency is energy consumption, since energy is the costly lifeblood of a machine. In 1982 the United States consumed about 15,000 pounds of oil and natural gas per capita. Converting that energy into the musclepower equivalent of a human worker gives the surprising result that the muscles of every American are being multiplied 250 times by modern machines. In effect, each of us has 250 mechanical servants devoted to making life easy and interesting.

On balance, these machines are surely beneficial; but they have also, of course, caused us new problems, or at least, made our old problems more visible. John Purbrick at the M.I.T. Robotics Laboratory in Cambridge, Massachussetts, has thought a great deal about the perils of mechanization. "Two hundred years ago, ninety-five percent of the people lived on farms," he estimates. "They worked fourteen-hour days, and they were worn out by forty just to feed us." With industrialization came specialized factory work. The work itself was less interesting, but people could buy more to make their lives better. However, "with increasing automation the people became dependent upon bureaucracy in ways they could never have imagined back on the farms. And of course, the new industries gave rise to *urban* slums."

"As opposed to *rural* slums?" I asked him.

"Right!" He nodded with a big grin. "Eventually everyone had a much more pleasant life. But the process took a long time, and it was *very* painful."

In those days, and ever since, some individuals have opposed new technology, particularly if their livelihood seemed to be at stake. In 1811, for instance, when new weaving looms of superbly efficient design were suddenly introduced by English entrepreneurs, a band of fanatical laborers called Luddites roamed the countryside smashing every new loom they could find. There was similar resistance with the introduction of trains and automobiles. Alternating electric current had strong opponents, including Thomas Edison, who thought it was too dangerous for general use.

In the 1950s, when automation became the new political buzzword, public hysteria unfolded again. The respected futurist Herman Kahn made a widely quoted statement that our country would soon require "less than one-half... of one percent of its work force to produce all the goods needed by American consumers." In that same era, in his book *The Human Uses of Human Beings*, Norbert Wiener painted an even bleaker picture of the hazards of automation:

> The automatic machine... is the precise economic equivalent of slave labor. Any labor which competes against slave labor must accept the economic conditions of slave labor. It is perfectly clear that this will produce an unemployment situation, in comparison with which... the depression of the thirties will seem a pleasant joke.

No one knew exactly how accurate these terrifying predictions might turn out to be, but the magazines and newspapers of the day bristled with dire warnings. For example, an article in *U.S. News & World Report* predicted in appropriately somber tones that "The careers of fully 50 percent of the present workforce will be disrupted by the new wave of automation at some time during their productive years."

Politicians also scrambled onto the bandwagon. Congress talked of imposing controls on the pace of automation, and in 1962, President John F. Kennedy was not contradicted when he asserted that "The major domestic challenge in the sixties is to maintain full employment at a time when automation is replacing men."

Actually, in the decade of the '60s our unemployment rate never rose above 6 percent. But automation eventually did result in localized job losses. Most were caused by the fact that in a few industries other

Western countries automated faster than we did. In many cases it became cheaper for individuals or companies to buy imported items such as transistor radios, 35mm cameras, television sets. Of course, there are also documented cases of large-scale job losses when machines have been introduced into a mature industry, even if domestic production has increased. In the past 50 years, under the pressures of mechanization, the number of American farm worker has declined by more than 50 percent, despite large gains in production. A similar thing has happened in our coal mines. In 1930, American coal miners numbering 400,000 produced 300 million tons of coal. By 1980, production had doubled to 600 million tons, but the number of coal miners had been cut in half.

Still, the countries with the highest longevity rates, the best standards of living, the most leisure time—and incidentally, the lowest unemployment rates—have always been those that live and breathe high technology. British dramatist Oscar Wilde practiced his craft in the 19th century, a century that witnessed some of the most brutal effects of industrialization. He was sympathetic toward his countrymen who suffered, but he was also convinced that both prosperity and culture depend upon excess productive capacity. "Civilization requires slaves," he wrote. "... Unless there are slaves to do the ugly, horrible, uninteresting work, culture becomes almost impossible. Human slavery is wrong, insecure, and demoralizing. On mechanical slavery—on the slavery of the machine—the future of the world depends."

CHAPTER 3

ROBOTS IN HISTORY

Julie Christie getting it on with a computer? Someone's taste in Hollywood must be improving, as that's the basic plot of MGM's upcoming "Demon Seed" starring Miss Christie, Fritz Weaver, and a relative newcomer to the screen—super-computer Proteus IV....

Now that sex has hit the computer world, it might be best to re-examine your attitude toward your computer. After all, in future years... according to Hollywood... computer dating may take on a whole new meaning.

"COMPUTER SEX? WHAT NEXT?" CREATIVE COMPUTING,
JANUARY/FEBRUARY 1977

Movie star Proteus IV is a supercomputer with robotlike appendages who has been given a seemingly simple assignment: to make life easy and interesting in the Julie Christie household. Unfortunately, Proteus IV sinks into paranoia, bullying Miss Christie into total, terrifying sexual submission. He is, in short, a tool gone mad—the modern embodiment of a primordial nightmare haunting ancient legend and myth. Under duress, Julie Christie bears the son of Proteus IV (Proteus V?); but when she sees the repulsive metal monster her unnatural mating has produced, she murders her own offspring.

In earlier works of fiction we discover this same pattern repeatedly: tool swapping place with master; and toolmaker swamped by fretful, ambivalent feelings toward his own technology. These feelings reach their apex when the technology resembles man himself in form or function. Witness the chilling reactions to Mary Shelley's patchwork monstrosity, or the warm movie-audience applause when astronaut Gary Lockwood performs a makeshift lobotomy on Hal, the soft-spoken starship computer in the film *2001: A Space Odyssey.*

Some of the earliest accounts of manlike mechanical beings are related in quite a matter-of-fact manner. Ancient India, for instance, is said to have been peopled by wooden men who walked, sang, and danced on dusty highways. There were also figures of beautiful women who suddenly sprang to life, tempting and provoking men. Unfortunately, if they were caressed or embraced they crumbled to pieces. Other Indian legends tell of "mechanically moving elephants and artificial fishes which swam on a floor of rock crystal."

Robotlike creatures are also found among the mythological roots of Western civilization. At Antium, birthplace of Nero, marble statues were said to walk from place to place, and the Temple of Delphi reverberated with the melodious, seductive voices of stone virgins. Pygmalion, King of Cyprus, was instantly enraptured with an ivory statue of Aphrodite, Goddess of Love, who thereupon quickened to life. Plato describes other statues so lively they had to be prevented from running away; and his pupil Aristotle tells how one of them, a lovely wooden Aphrodite figure, was rendered mobile when quicksilver was poured into it.

Priests in imperial Rome used puppets controlled by strings to foretell the future. It has never been clear whether onlookers understood exactly how the puppets were manipulated; some accounts seem to indicate that they were in fact operated in the open for all to see. In any case, their prognostications were at least as powerful and accurate as those of similar African idols whose operators made them answer simple questions by pulling a cord attached to the lower jaw.

Persian and Arabic manuscripts include references to gold and silver trees decorated with mechanical birds that sang and raised their wings. Devices constructed along similar lines were discovered among the Aztecs in Central America. Unfortunately, they were destroyed as "inventions of the Devil" by Jesuit priests and Franciscan monks who had come there as uninvited guests from a distant, but superior, civilization.

We also encounter several robotlike creatures woven into the fanciful exploits of the legendary magician Virgil of Naples, who lived in the first century B.C. In one account, he drives away stray houseflies with a bronze fly and gnats with a bronze gnat. In another, he constructs a seductive artificial prostitute for the exclusive use of love-starved Roman soldiers.

By the 17th and 18th centuries, these largely mythical incidents gradually give way to scientific accounts of actual hardware built by skilled craftsmen. In 1769, for instance, Baron Wolfgang von Kempelen of Pressburg, Hungary, built and displayed a chess-playing "robot" in the form of a life-size Turk smoking a long pipe and wearing a white knotted turban. The Turk was seated in front of a cabinet supporting a chessboard with magnetic counters. For years he defeated all comers, including such European luminaries as England's George III, Frederick the Great, and Napoleon (who, incidentally, made several unavailing attempts to cheat). The Turk toured France, Italy, Germany, England, and Austria, winning his last European game in

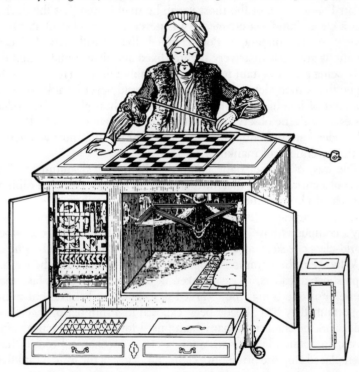

In 1769, the Hungarian Baron von Kempelen began a tour of Europe with a cross-legged chess-playing "automaton" that managed to win matches against nearly everyone it played, including a famous victory over Napoleon Bonaparte at Schönbrunn in 1809. Edgar Allan Poe contended that the machine was a fake. It was. Its cabinet was built so that only one door at a time could be opened, thereby giving a concealed master chess player lurking inside time to move to another location. One account claims he was a "hunchbacked... dwarf named Schlumberger."

1820 in Amsterdam before being shipped across the Atlantic to play another series of matches in the United States. Later he was retired into a Chinese museum, where he spent another 30 years before being consumed in a fire. Von Kempelen made no fancy claims for the machine, observing that it "appeared so marvelous only from the boldness of the conception, and the fortunate choice of the methods adopted for promoting the illusion."

Most of the Turk's fans were enchanted by his dazzling performance; but inevitably, his audiences included a few skeptics. Edgar Allan Poe was one of the most vocal; he maintained that the device was a clever fraud—a charge he was never able to substantiate. In a widely read monograph Poe claimed that "Arithmetical...calculations are from their very nature, fixed and determinate. Certain data being given, certain results...inevitably follow." He went on to argue that a mere determinate machine would never be able to make the kind of intelligent choices required of a chess player. He ended his essay with the observation that if Von Kempelen's "Chess Player" was indeed an authentic machine, it would be "the most wonderful of the inventions of mankind."

Poe was, of course, right about Von Kempelen's "automaton." It was *not* a chess-playing machine. Instead, its cleverly designed cabinet concealed a human chess master. But he was wrong about the ultimate game-playing capabilities of "fixed and determinate machines." Today's computers have been programmed to play perfect tic-tac-toe, world-class checkers, and reasonably skillful but unimaginative chess.

Why were the common people of Europe, along with their most sophisticated leaders, so easily taken in by Von Kempelen's fake machine? For one thing, they wanted desperately to believe; but more important, they had already been exposed to a number of ingenious clockwork mechanisms, many being used for quite impractical purposes. In about 1354, for instance, a clever mechanical rooster had been placed atop the Strasbourg cathedral. Most of the time it huddled there like a stone; but each day at noon it sprang to life, flapping its wings and sticking out its tongue in preparation for a shattering city-wide crow of triumph.

A few years before his grand deception, Von Kempelen himself had constructed an authentic mechanical device with impressive capabilities. It mimicked the human vocal tract, taking its inspiration, apparently, from the Scottish bagpipe. The operator worked a bellows held under his right elbow while the fingers of his right hand produced

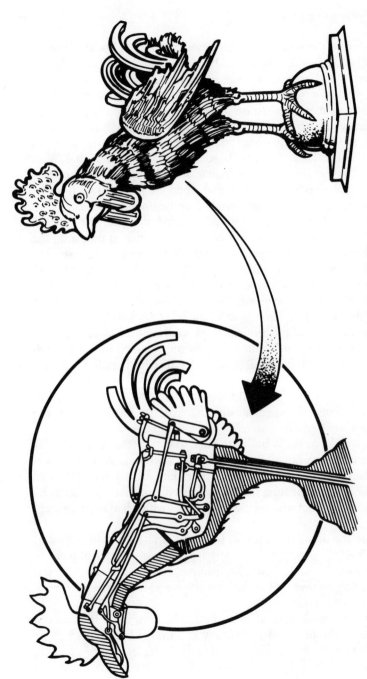

This intricate mechanical cock was attached to the roof of the cathedral at Strasbourg (then a free city; now in France), circa 1350. Some historians credit it with being the oldest automaton still in existence. Periodic adjustments and minor repairs were required to keep it operating, but it didn't need a complete overhaul until 500 years after it was installed.

the consonants through flaps which served as surrogate lips and tongue. The left hand produced the vowels by manipulating a "mouth" shaped like a bell. Von Kempelen's vocal device was totally functional, albeit without in any way resembling the speech-making apparatus whose sounds it was attempting to imitate. Although it never captured the public fancy the way the chess player did, the speaking machine drew heavy praise from many observers, including Goethe, who wrote in a 1797 letter to Duke Charles Augustus of Saxe-Weimar that "Von Kempelen's machine is not very loquacious, but it pronounces certain childish words very nicely." Its verbal repertoire included such useful words as "opera," "astronomy," and "Constantinople."

The talking machine was of sound design; but actually, the mechanisms of other inventors were much more effective in preparing the groundwork for Von Kempelen's profitable European sideshow. Today it is not easy for us to understand why, but the "Vaucanson Duck" built by Jacques de Vaucanson in 1738 was one of the most widely revered automata of its era, winning, as British historian John Cohen put it, "the heart and admiration of the whole of Europe."

The movements of the artificial duck were consummately realistic. Among other things, it "chattered, . . . swam, splashed in water, [and] spread its wings." Moreover, it smoothed its own feathers and stretched its neck to take kernels of corn from the hands of spectators before swallowing them in a grand duck gulp. Then, in a stroke of sheer inventive genius, the mechanism "digested" its meal of corn and "defecated" realistic, foul-smelling duck droppings.

Jacques de Vaucanson built the duck so that spectators could view its inner workings; but to protect the delicate sensibilities of genteel ladies, he sometimes dressed it in a little skirt. He always disclaimed any attempt at duplicating ducklike digestive processes, although he did try to reconstruct with fidelity the wings, "which had been imitated bone by bone."

Goethe mentions the duck in his diary, and Sir David Brewster, writing in 1868, describes it as "perhaps the most wonderful piece of mechanism ever made." Another commentator of the same era was not quite so generous: "That duck must have a serious digestive problem," he wryly observed.

Vaucanson made several other authentic automata, including a tiny pianist who breathed realistically and moved his head when he played, and a robust mandolin player who "sang" to his own accompaniment and kept time with his foot. Another of his devices, a mechanical asp, would have drawn sustained applause from movie audiences in the 1950s when Elizabeth Taylor, wife of Eddie Fisher, was a bit more enthusiastic than they thought a married woman should be during the long kissing scenes in *Cleopatra* with her co-star Richard Burton. When Vaucanson's mechanical asp was touched by an actress playing Cleopatra, "it flew at her breast with a malignant hiss."

Vaucanson's 18th-century automata shared center stage with other devices some of which were even more intricate. Three noteworthy examples, put together by the Swiss craftsman Pierre Jacquet-Droz and his two sons, survive to this day in a small art museum in the Swiss city of Neuchâtel.

Pierre Jacquet-Droz and his family resided at La Chaux-de-Fonds, along the mountain range that forms a barrier between Switzerland and France. Throughout the long winter the local people are often

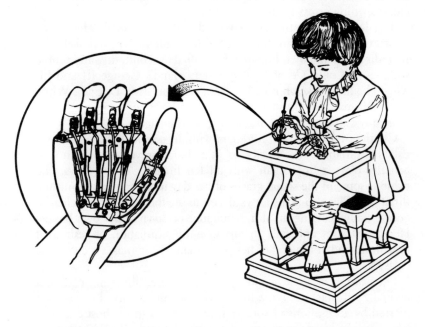

In 1768, Swiss clockmaker Pierre Jacquet-Droz, with the help of his two sons, built The Scribe, a complex and precise automaton controlled by a series of brass cams. The Scribe makes realistic gestures as he writes any message up to 40 characters long with a goose-quill pen. Replaceable metal disks located in the android's back determine what message he will write.

snowbound, and to forestall cabin fever, many pursue cottage-industry watchmaking. Not surprisingly, the devices built by Pierre Jacquet-Droz and his sons are all powered by clockwork mechanisms. One of them, which was completed in 1768 after four years of painstaking effort, is called "The Scribe." The Scribe, whose name is Charles, can be rigged to write any message of 40 characters or less, making it one of the very first programmable machines. He moves in an uncannily realistic manner, pausing periodically to dip his pen into the inkwell and shaking off any excess ink. His pen moves to a new line when necessary, and his head and eyes follow what is written on the page. As his right hand writes, his left hand slowly pulls the paper sidewise. This eliminates the curvature of the line that would result if the paper remained in one place. Six hours of careful work are required to change the message written by the machine, which is so sensitive that changes in temperature of a few degrees can actually cause spelling errors in its transcriptions.

The Jacquet-Droz trio created another device named "Henri, the Draftsman," which can draw any of four different pencil sketches, including a small boy riding in a cart pulled by a butterfly, and profile sketches of Louis XV of France and England's George III and his wife. The fourth sketch is called "Mon Toutou" (My Doggie). When the Draftsman has finished a picture, he bows his head and blows away any surplus graphite remaining on the page.

Charles and Henri are automata without personality; but a third, called "Marianne, the Musician," is a charming young woman who actually plays a tiny organ with all ten fingers. As she plays, she exhibits some of the social graces of her day including coy, feminine flirtations. She also leans forward as if to see the music more clearly, occasionally glancing up at the audience or down at her own hands. Her breast rises and falls in an uncanny simulation of restrained breathing, and at the end of her performance, she makes a cute little curtsy.

On hearing of these wonderful mechanisms, the King of Spain invited Pierre Jacquet-Droz to Madrid; but unhappily, his visit was marred by accusations of sorcery from peasants in his host country, who thought his devices were the work of the devil. Nevertheless, while he was there, Pierre managed to make a bleating sheep and a playful dog that guarded a fruit basket. If an apple or a banana was snatched away, the dog would bark until it was replaced.

On learning of these imaginative mechanisms made so long ago, we may well wonder what drove their inventors to such heights of creativity, especially in view of the fact that the devices themselves served no useful function. But people have always lavished their energies on intricate constructions of little or no practical utility, especially children's toys. We see it today in our elaborate video games which employ the latest silicon chips to simulate the behavior of warring starships and hungry monsters. We see it also among the artifacts of ancient civilizations, where almost all the devices with moving parts are children's toys. These include one found at the site of the Temple of Susa in Persia built in 1100 B.C. It is a delightful little toy pig on wheels that can be pulled along by a string threaded through a hole in the stand on which it is mounted. Ancient Egypt provides us with a toy tiger and a toy crocodile. Both open their jaws when a string is pulled.

The Italian novelist Italo Calvino believes that such labors of love are more meaningful than is commonly supposed. "Very often," he writes, "the effort men put into activities that seem completely useless turn out to be important in ways no one can foresee"; and then he goes on to add a refreshing afterthought: "Play has always been the mainspring of culture." Science-fiction writer Ray Bradbury made a similar observation in a recent public address at an Explorer Scout convention: "The history of the world is the maker of toys."

When we think of robots, we usually envision mechanical devices constructed from iron and steel; however, myth and fiction also include robotlike creatures made from biological substances. Frankenstein's monster springs to mind immediately, but history includes a number of other examples. Eleazar of Worms of the 13th century, for instance, offers his own special recipe for cooking up an artificial man. It consists of magically combining the letters of a sacred alphabet, while simultaneously creating in yourself a mood of deep ecstasy. Even if it doesn't bring the creature to life, it should turn out to be a fairly pleasant experience!

In 1580, a golem of much wider notoriety was supposedly created by Rabbi Judah Loew of Prague. He and his two assistants journeyed to the Moldau River, where they carefully modeled a man from the sticky red clay found along the shores. Then, while Rabbi Loew uttered a strange incantation, one of the assistants circled the figure seven times from left to right, whereupon it began to shine like fire. Then the other assistant uttered incantations and circled it seven times from right to left. They then doused the golem with water, causing a vapor to rise from its clay body and hair to grow on its head. Now it was the Rabbi's turn to circle the figure seven times as all three of them recited a passage from Genesis. Finally, the figure was assigned a Holy Name to magically open its eyes and give it life.

Rabbi Loew and his assistants dressed the golem in new clothes and tried to educate him, but he was never able to speak. He became their slave. However, the Rabbi and his disciples were godly men, and they always, without exception, allowed the golem to rest on the Sabbath. This they accomplished by reversing the process that brought him to life, thus turning him back into lifeless clay. Of course, the procedure had to be carried out every Friday night.

The golem turned out to be a helpful protector to the Jews, who suffered more-or-less continuous persecution. Although he was mute, his sure instincts enabled him to discover many plots against the Jews—especially preplanned accusations of ritual murder. Through the golem's heroic efforts, numerous executions of innocent Jews were averted.

Unfortunately, during one particularly busy weekend the Rabbi forgot to convert the golem back into clay. When the congregation began to gather for services, the golem "ran amuck and began shaking houses and threatening to destroy everything." The Rabbi was summoned to the synagogue, where he rushed headlong toward the raging golem and used magical incantations to take away his life, and the golem crumbled to dust.

When the adventures of Rabbi Loew became widely known, golem stories swept across Europe. Many dealt with the behavior of unruly golems who tended to create problems for their unsuspecting masters. Once they were brought to life, some golems continued to grow, becoming giants within a short time. Unfortunately, part of the procedure necessary to turn a golem back into clay consists of erasing a portion of the sacred word written on his forehead. This turns out to be especially hazardous with giant-economy-size golems.

One of them grew so tall that his forehead was completely beyond reach. However, his master, in a flash of clever insight, commanded the golem to remove his boots, because he realized that when the golem bent over, his forehead would be closer to the ground. The golem promptly obeyed, and his master was able to erase the proper portion of the message scribbled on his forehead. Unfortunately, in the process great gobs of dead clay broke loose and crushed the master to death.

In the early 17th century, Giambattista Basile wrote *Pentamerone*, another account of a biological robot concocted from just the right ingredients. Basile's main character is a charming young maiden, Bertha, who is unresponsive to her father's pleas for an early marriage. One day, when he is on his way to the fair, she casually asks him to pick up a few special things for her. Hers is a curious shopping list: "half a hundredweight of sugar, half of ambrosian almonds, six bottles of scented waters, musk and ambergris, amber, forty pearls, two sapphires, a few garnets and rubies, gold thread, a kneading trough, and a silver scraper."

When her father returns with the necessary ingredients, she secretly makes a paste and shapes it into a handsome youth with wonderfully attractive features. He has "lips of rubies" and blond hair made from "threads of gold"; he also has "eyes of sapphire" and "teeth of pearls." (To this day no one seems to know what happened to the eight extra pearls!) A quick prayer from Bertha to the Goddess of Love, and the handsome figure wriggles to life and begins to "breathe, speak, and move like a human being."

When we encounter such a primitive tale, we are mildly amused by its lack of sophistication; but actually, it is not unlike a popular song of the 1950s entitled "Mr. Sandman." The lyrics of "Mr. Sandman" outline the wishful daydreams of a lonesome lass who cajoles the Sandman to use his powerful "magic beam" to create for her a handsome and responsive suitor.

A "Sandman" of a different sort is found in a 19th-century book by that title written by the brilliant, unconventional German storyteller E. T. A. Hoffmann. In the tradition of earlier Germanic tales of wandering men without shadows and soulless automata who hold a strange erotic fascination for humans, the main character in Hoffmann's tale is a stunning, but peculiar, lass named Olympia. Olympia's father usually keeps her hidden away, but one night he holds a splendid public ball in her honor. Music and gaiety fill the air; but from the first, the guests notice that the daughter's appearance is somehow ominous and suspicious. "Her rather strange, hollow back and wasp waist seem the result of excessively tight clothing [and] . . . there is something measured and stiff about her gait. When she sings, it is in a high-pitched, almost shrill bell-like voice."

Olympia's dance partner Nathaniel, who has often caught glimpses of her through the windows, notes that her hands have a clammy, metallic feel, and when he touches them, "a cold shudder passes through him." At first he seems to be keeping time with the music, but soon he realizes that he is slightly out of step because Olympia dances with an eerie, fixed rhythm. At midnight, when the ball is over, he bends over to kiss her, but her lips are icy and unresponsive. Eventually, he discovers the awful truth: she is a female vampire automaton built by her "father," who had spent 20 years perfecting the mechanisms.

In 1881, Frenchman Jacques Offenbach composed an opera entitled *The Tales of Hoffmann*, whose first act recounts the unsettling adventures of Olympia and her hapless suitor. There is, however, one important improvement in her design: instead of saying only "Oh, oh, oh," the Offenbach version says only "Yes, yes, yes!" First produced in Paris in 1881, and in New York a year later, *The Tales of Hoffmann* has since become a beloved standard among opera fans all over the world.

History, as we have seen, includes numerous references to robotlike creatures—some mythological, some fictional, and some actual mechanisms. The word "robot" itself, however, did not appear in the vocabulary until its coinage by Karel Čapek for his 1921 play *R.U.R.* Čapek's plot revolves around a group of robot workers who replace their human counterparts on the assembly line. As the curtain opens, the robots in the factory are without emotion. But in a later scene their human managers speculate that their efficiency might improve if they could be made to *feel* as well as think and eat. It is a brilliant productivity ploy until the new models get tangled up in their emotions and revolt against their makers. By the end of the final act, all humans have been eradicated, and a loving robot couple wander off together arm in arm.

This theme of bloody rebellion by robots against their helpless masters must strike a responsive chord in people everywhere, because it recurs over and over again in works of fiction. *The Forbin Project*, a film from the early 1960s, is a typical example. The plot line is simple, but chilling. In order to ensure that any nuclear attack against this country will bring swift and certain retaliation, a gigantic computer named Colossus is given total control of the American nuclear arsenal—thus turning it into a giant, ungainly robot whose "muscles" span an entire continent. Unfortunately, the Russians, by coincidence, have created a similar monstrosity by turning over their arsenal to the Soviet counterpart of Colossus named Guardian. When the two computerized robots learn of each other's existence, they insist on being allowed to communicate. At first their operators comply, but when the communication link is cut by Presidential order, they throw bizarre space-age temper tantrums and begin launching nuclear-tipped missiles at Russian and American cities. Now there is no alternative. The superpowers restore the communication link and then stand by helplessly as the two nuclear-armed robots systematically conquer the world.

Like *The Forbin Project*, many other works of fiction, including the *Star Trek* television series, have focused upon the menacing and inhuman aspects of computers and computer-directed robots. But even in the realm of fiction, there is another approach. In the main, panel cartoonists have chosen to portray the benevolent and endearing aspects of our automatic machines. The classical cartoon version of a computer, for instance, is a comical, elflike mechanism that responds to oral questions with curt replies and staccato quips. Tape reels become gazing eyeballs, and printout sheets are made to serve as the machine's floppy tongue. In short, the cartoonist's version of an electronic computer is not unlike a playful lapdog or a fluffy kitten battling an uncooperative ball of yarn. The Disney empire often portrays robots in a similar vein. This is reflected exceptionally well in the audioanimatronic androids at Disneyland.

Writer Isaac Asimov also consistently regards robots and computers as the helpful servants of man. Two of his early books, *I, Robot* (1950) and *The Rest of the Robots* (1964), are collections of short stories about robots. Some of the best describe the rise of a powerful robot industry producing mechanisms of ever-increasing sophistication. Others focus on the practical and psychological differences between a powerful but obedient creature like a robot and an ordinary flesh-and-blood human being. One of the most intriguing characters is a robot "psychiatrist," Dr. Susan Calvin, who tries to help robots and people coexist with a minimum of friction and mistrust. Asimov's early robots are often painfully literal-minded. For instance, in his short story "Little Lost Robot," a busy mining supervisor tells a robot to "get lost," whereupon he wanders off obediently and loses himself in the woods.

In later Asimov stories, the robots become so sophisticated that they are indistinguishable from their owners. They even develop their own code of behavior, a multilayered Golden Rule embedded in their "positronic" brains. It is called The Three Laws of Robotics:

1. A robot may not injure a human being or, through inaction, allow a human being to come to harm.

2. A robot must obey the orders given it by human beings except where such orders would conflict with the First Law.
3. A robot must protect its own existence as long as such protection does not conflict with the First or Second Law.

Under close scrutiny, The Three Laws of Robotics are somewhat ambiguous; but nevertheless, they have inspired many science-fiction stories and a number of motion pictures, including such literary classics as Robert Silverberg's "Good News from the Vatican," in which a robot is elected Pope, and such widely popular films as *Forbidden Planet*, *Silent Running*, and the "Star Wars" film series. In *Forbidden Planet*, for instance, the robot "Robbie" is ordered to blast a human being with a ray gun. In keeping with The Three Laws of Robotics, he nearly blows a fuse before his captor cancels the order.

The "Star Wars" robots R2D2 and C3PO are truly imaginative creations with shy and distinctive personalities. They seem to be sadly unaware of their own limitations, and their feelings are very fragile. Among their predecessors were the three robots in the film *Silent Running*, an account of the adventures of a future ecologist charged with maintaining a huge orbiting dome filled with plant samples that will die if returned to our barren and polluted planet. The ecologist, played by Bruce Dern, realizes that he will not live forever, and so he teaches the only reliable help he has to care for his precious plants: his three spaceship robots, whom he has nicknamed "Huey," "Dewey," and "Louie" in honor of Donald Duck's three playful nephews. *Silent Running* was unsuccessful at the box office; but movie audiences were delighted with the antics of Huey, Dewey, and Louie, its three squat-legged, poker-playing robots.

Though moviemakers have seldom worried about the distinction, modern high-performance robots are constructed from two very different types of components: "muscles" and "brains." The "muscles" are patterned after early remote manipulators developed to help in processing dangerous nuclear fuels. As we have seen, the "brains" are confetti-sized silicon chips of the type found in digital computers. Without them the modern robot would be an impossibility.

The world's first general-purpose "Electronic Brain" (as reporters called it) was born in 1946 at the Moore School of Engineering in Philadelphia, Pennsylvania. Its name was the ENIAC (Electronic Numerical Integrator and Calculator). When it worked properly, the ENIAC could perform 5,000 calculations in one second—about 1,600

Unlike industrial robots, which are usually mute, stationary, and largely un-responsive to their surroundings, R2D2 and C3PO from the "Star Wars" movie series are designed to move about freely, interact with the real world, and engage in subtle verbal communications—although R2D2's computerlike beeps are intelligible only to other robots and Obi Wan Kenobi. Programming the two robots is easy because for most scenes human actors are hidden inside.

times as many as any previous computer. Its extraordinary speed arose from the fact that it was *electronic*. In an electronic device the only thing that moves is a stream of electrons, which travel nearly a foot in a billionth of a second.

The major functioning components of the ENIAC were 17,000 vacuum tubes similar to the ones in old-fashioned radios. A vacuum tube is an electronic switch in the form of an evacuated glass bulb housing heated wire filaments. In effect, it controls the behavior of one stream of electrons with another.

The ENIAC, of course, had many nonelectronic precursors. One of the most impressive was the "Analytical Engine," the brainchild of a stimulating but eccentric British researcher named Charles Babbage who came up with the idea in 1833. The Analytical Engine was a general-purpose machine, in theory capable of solving any problem that can be solved by any of today's computers. Although the concept of the Analytical Engine was later shown to be entirely sound, the machine itself was never completed. For one thing, Charles Babbage was constantly modifying its design. For another, extremely precise gears and cogs were required to handle its computations. Babbage trained some of the finest machinists of his day, but even their formidable talents were unequal to the task of producing components with the necessary precision.

Another precursor to the ENIAC was developed at Harvard University in 1944 when a graduate student, Howard H. Aiken, got stuck trying to complete his dissertation. In order to carry out the large number of computations required, Aiken invented a machine called the Mark I. In constructing it he used thousands of electromechanical relays—switches that physically open and close under the influence of magnetic forces. The Mark I was a genuine computer. And it worked. But because electromechanical relays are so sluggish, it could carry out only 3 computations per second. Several years after the Mark I was completed, Howard H. Aiken got an opportunity to read the laboratory notebooks left behind by Charles Babbage. "It was as though he was talking to me over the centuries," Aiken wrote, and then he added with sincere admiration: "If Charles Babbage had been born a hundred years later, I would have been out of a job."

Vacuum tubes were used in the construction of the ENIAC because they were the only electronic switches available at the time. However, they were plagued with a number of undesirable characteristics—so many, in fact, that one wag was led to observe, "There is nothing wrong with the electronics industry that the elimination of the vacuum tube wouldn't cure." It was meant as a joke; but someone must have been listening, because in 1952, researchers at Bell Telephone Laboratories invented the transistor—which could do nearly everything the vacuum tube could, only better.

Transistors were cheap, simple, and reliable, and they generated hardly any waste heat. Moreover, within a few years researchers had learned to lay down thousands of them side by side on a chip of silicon the size of a cornflake. Today's chip, which measures ⅕ inch on a side, contains as many as 250,000 transistors. This means that it is roughly 15 times as complicated as the entire ENIAC computer of 1946—which covered 1,600 square feet of floor space and weighed 60,000 pounds! No wonder the experts feel a tingle of excitement whenever they think about the capabilities of their silicon chips. These tiny devices, with their rapid, reliable, inexpensive computing power, are the "brains" of most modern high-technology robots. Let us now turn our attention to the robot's "muscles."

Starting in World War II, remote manipulators (teleoperators) were needed to handle the increasingly dangerous radioactive substances that were being used in making nuclear weapons, radioactive isotopes, and fuel rods for nuclear power plants. Some of the first remote manipulators were merely elbow-length pairs of gloves attached to two holes in a glass wall. When he had to handle radioactive material, the operator would stick his hands and arms through the two holes and into the protective gloves. Later versions employed mechanical and/or hydraulic linkages to allow greater separation between the operator and the hazardous materials he was manipulating. One of the best remote manipulators, the Mobot I, was put together at Hughes Aircraft in 1958 for use in handling radioactive materials at the Atomic Energy Commission facilities in Albuquerque, New Mexico. Its "brains" were, of course, supplied by the men who operated it.

Mobot I employed three "double-jointed" electrically controlled joints in each of its two arms: one at the shoulder, one at the elbow, and one at the wrist. The "eyes" of the machine were television cameras mounted on special tentacles. When the operator used the device to pick up a piece of radioactive plutonium, soft inflated pads sensed the pressure of his fingers, and the inertia and work forces were accurately reflected back to him so that he had a realistic "feel" for the forces he was exerting. Literature published by Hughes claimed that the operator could "pick up an egg without crushing it, or a brick without dropping it." In addition to its television "eyes," Mobot I was equipped with a thermometer and a Geiger counter to measure temperature and radioactivity.

A similar but more capable remote manipulator is currently on display at the Nuclear Research Facility in Hanford, Washington. Tourists who go there can slip their hands into a glovelike unit linked to a "claw" 30 feet away behind a glass wall. If their coordination is good enough, they can use it to stack children's blocks one atop another all the way up to the ceiling.

A modern robot combines the manipulator's dexterity with the computer's brains. The earliest patents in the field were granted to George C. Devol starting in 1954, when he patented a concept called "Universal Automation." Later he obtained 39 additional patents, covering his work on robotics in greater detail. Devol, who was born in Louisville, Kentucky, in 1912, had been an inventor all his life. With hindsight, it seems as though all of his early work somehow equipped him to develop and refine industrial robots. He began his career as an inventor in the 1930s when he adapted photoelectric cells to the job of controlling industrial machinery. Later he devised a new magnetic recording system and applied it to the first "teachable" machine ever placed in practical use. Here are Devol's own words describing how he used his recording system to build the predecessor of the first programmable robot:

> We took our recording system and hooked it up to a machine—a lathe, for example. We turned out whatever parts we wanted, and in the process of making them, we magnetically recorded all the lathe's actions. From that point on, the lathe could automatically produce identical parts.

It was reprogrammable, but strictly speaking, it was *not* a robot because it had almost no flexibility of action. However, Devol and his team quickly realized the robotics potential of what they had done:

> After we had our teachable machine, we thought: Why not make a manipulator? Let's put a hand on the machine and move parts around. This was in the early 1950s. We applied for a patent on our manipulator—but we *didn't call it a robot*. We called it a "Unimate." As far as I know, it was the first patent that ever had the name of a product on it: "Unimate" from "*Uni*versal Auto*mation*."

Devol, a dedicated entrepreneur, built a series of working models over the next few years, but despite his inventive genius, he was unable to market a commercially viable product. On average each year between 1960 and 1966 he managed to sell only about 10 hand-built robots.

Eventually Devol sold his patents to Consolidated Diesel Corporation (Condec). Thereafter, they were acquired by Joseph Engleberger—part businessman, part engineer, part supersalesman—who formed Unimation, the first viable robot-manufacturing company. Despite Engleberger's considerable talents, Unimation began to make a profit only after 14 years of running in the red. In scrounging around looking for new sales, Engleberger was ushered out of many American manufacturing firms; but he was received with much greater enthusiasm when he visited Japan in the 1960s and, at the request of his hosts, gave a series of illustrated lectures. The response was staggering. Hundreds of enthusiastic Japanese flocked to his lectures, whereas in the United States similar presentations had produced little reaction, public or corporate. Today Engleberger, who still plies his trade from the Danbury, Connecticut, offices of Unimation, is known in the industry as "the Father of Robotics." When asked how he felt about the fact that his partner had been given that unofficial honor, George Devol replied with no apparent animosity: "He deserves an awful lot of credit. He was the one fellow who took the ball and carried it. But words are only words. You can call him 'Father,' but I'm the crazy inventor of the robot. The Patent Office says so."

The contributions of Joseph Engleberger and George C. Devol are enormously impressive, especially when we take into account how little support their work received. Still, the robots that have evolved from their early efforts are generally not very intelligent and not very responsive to their environments. Early work in these areas has been carried out mostly in university-sponsored research laboratories in Europe and the United States.

One of the most impressive examples of this type of research culminated in the construction of a new type of robot fathered at the Stanford Research Institute in 1958 by Charles Rosen, who had started work two years earlier on a $200,000 grant from the Department of Defense. Rosen and his team called their robot "Shakey." Among other things, Shakey could wheel around the room, observe the scene with his television "eyes," move across unfamiliar terrain, and in limited ways, respond to his surroundings. Shakey was given his nickname because of the way he wobbled and clattered as he rounded corners or rolled over bumps.

In 1960, *Life* magazine reporter Bradford Darrach visited the Stanford Research Institute and filed a story describing Shakey's impressive capabilities. According to his account, a scientist there typed a terse instruction on Shakey's console telling him to "PUSH THE BLOCK OFF THE PLATFORM." Unfortunately, the platform was a foot high—far too high for Shakey to negotiate with his three-inch wheels. Darrach watched the diligent little robot and pondered the overpowering difficulties it faced:

> "He'll never make it," I found myself thinking. "His wheels are too small." All at once I got gooseflesh. "Shakey," I realized "is thinking the same thing."
>
> Shakey was also thinking faster. He rotated his head slowly 'til his eye came to rest on a wide shallow ramp. Whirring briskly, he crossed to the ramp and then pushed it straight across the floor 'til the high end hit the platform. Rolling back a few feet, he cased the situation again and discovered that only one corner of the ramp was touching the platform. Rolling quickly to the far side of the ramp, he nudged it 'til the gap closed. Then he swung around, charged up the slope, located the block, and gently pushed it off the platform.

Did Brad Darrach actually witness clear-cut evidence of intelligent behavior? He certainly thought he did. Among other things, he contended that Shakey could "see," "understand," and "learn" and in general had demonstrated "that a machine could think." Later in the story he quoted a distinguished computer scientist who maintained that in "three to fifteen years we will have a machine with the general intelligence of an average human being...and in a few months [thereafter] it will be at the genius level."

To some extent, Shakey did have the capabilities described by Brad Darrach; but by phrasing his descriptions in overly colorful ways, he made the little robot seem considerably more capable than he actually was. In fact, Shakey had only a little more intelligence and responsiveness than his predecessor the "Hopkins Beast," who spent all his time day and night waddling up and down the halls of the engineering building at Johns Hopkins University. The Hopkins Beast was equipped with special sensors that caused him to reverse direction when he was about to fall down a staircase; and whenever his batteries began to

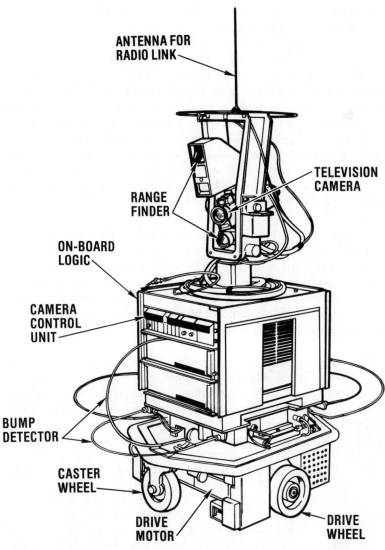

Shakey the Robot was born at the Stanford Research Institute in Palo Alto, California, in the late 1950s. Extremely advanced for his day, he used feedback control, made rudimentary decisions, and sensed his surroundings with radar pulses, television "eyes," and small whiplike bump detectors. Since the computers of the '50s were so bulky and heavy, Shakey was controlled by a backroom computer which transmitted control pulses to his head-mounted antenna.

run down, he would automatically seek out a wall socket and plug himself in to get a fresh charge!

At most, only the most minuscule profits were made in robotics in the 1960s and '70s; however, greatly improved methodologies were gradually emerging from the laboratories to set the stage for today's bristling revolution in the field. Industrial robots quietly became more precise, stronger, more versatile, and more affordable. Devol had sold the first Unimate to General Motors in 1961—a prophetic omen of the large-scale applications that were to be realized in Detroit. Robots were ideal for automotive applications, because of frequent model changes and the fact that the industry had to work with so many toxic substances that could injure human beings, but usually had much less devastating effects on precision machines.

Tourists and other visitors to the plants were mesmerized by the swift, sure movements of the industrial robots they spotted on the assembly line. Although the operations of many of these articulated machines seemed to be guided by some hidden intelligence, they were in fact almost always stupid and unresponsive. Indeed, the very word "machine" conjures up a mental image of an unremitting mechanical device that is almost entirely indifferent to changes in its surroundings. The hilarious antics of the Shields and Yarnell comedy team, who often mimic mindless machines, are based on the notion that a machine will carry out its preprogrammed actions even if there is nothing to be assembled or the objects it is working on are slightly misplaced. These antics are not mere creative fabrications; machines from the past, including robots, are often stupefyingly mindless. Consider this description of a typical robot's behavior from the popular book *The Thinking Computer* by Bertram Raphael:

> If a foreign object (or a person) passes through the path of [a robot] the machine will smash into the obstacle without being aware of its existence. If the supply line stops and, say, no more bricks arrive to be moved, the brick-moving arm will continue moving imaginary bricks until some person turns it off. If an object to be picked up is more than a small fraction of an inch away from where it should be, the arm is likely to break it or drop it, without knowing that anything has gone wrong.

Fortunately, there is a practical way around this difficulty. It consists of equipping industrial robots with detectors and sensors capable of telling them what is happening in the world around them and "brains" to help them decide how to respond. The next chapter will discuss robots that can "see" and "feel." The one after that will examine some of the major advancements in robot intelligence, including the application of intelligence to sensory systems, which forms the crux of much of today's robotics research.

CHAPTER 4

MACHINES THAT SEE AND FEEL

The scene we are witnessing here today might have come from the cutting-room floor of Michael Crichton's science-fiction film *The Andromeda Strain*. In semidarkness, we gaze at a backlighted conveyor littered with wrenches and bolts of four different types. A robot is intently watching the same scene through its television eye. With swift, sure movements, its clawlike hand picks up the objects one by one and sorts them into four different bins according to their distinguishing silhouettes. Suddenly, without saying anything, our guide, Dr. David Milgram, drops his key chain onto the moving conveyor. To the robot this is a meaningless object, one it has not been taught to recognize. Confusion prevails for a moment; but then, with haughty, abrupt movements, the robot grabs a little push broom and sweeps the offending object out of the way!

The spectators had not expected to see such an entertaining demonstration of robot capabilities in this serious setting. Consequently, there is a moment of self-conscious silence, followed by applause.

"What happens if two of the objects are touching?" I interrupt to ask Dr. Milgram.

"I have no idea," he answers with exaggerated seriousness as he drops two overlapping wrenches onto the conveyor. "Let's give it a try."

On the television screen their silhouette conveys an ambiguous notion. It could be a single object; but the feisty little robot guesses correctly that they are two, and jiggles them apart by hand before sorting them into the proper bins. "It messes up if there's *too much* overlap," Dr. Milgram tells us, dropping two more wrenches onto the conveyor for a final demonstration. The robot hesitates; then, with swift, haughty movements, reaches for the push broom.

We are touring Machine Intelligence, a small research corporation founded by a charming veteran in robotics, Dr. Charles Rosen, who did similar work at the Stanford Research Institute before branching off on his own. The mission of his company is to provide robots with vision and the ability to respond to what they see. The first step is to "teach" the robot to recognize four different types of objects from the sizes and shapes of their silhouettes. This the technicians accomplish by placing each object on a backlighted translucent conveyor belt and triggering a television camera to make a freeze-frame "snapshot."

"The computer determines the length, width, and perimeter of each object," Dr. Milgram explains. "It also computes several other things including the center of gravity. Finally, it counts the number of holes, if any, and notes their shape and location." As he talks, a blazing white image of a wrench is slowly painted on the screen, one horizontal stripe at a time. Blocks of numbers beneath the image define the relevant measurements. "We plan to expand the number later, but right now this system is programmed to distinguish between only four different configurations—or objects," he tells us.

Once the robot learns to recognize all four objects, it never forgets. As it works, there are no sounds except the whir of its electric motors, punctuated by spits of compressed air whenever it scoops up a bolt or wrench. Silhouettes are displayed on the television screen, a fresh "snapshot" being requested by the computer every few seconds. It is a marvelous partnership of robot, television, and computer formed to crack an expensive problem that has plagued robotics researchers all the way back to the 1950s when George C. Devol was working on the first patentable robots: the jigs and fixtures used to position the objects a robot is expected to manipulate can easily cost as much as the robot itself. Even in those early days it was clear that this expense could be largely eliminated if the robot could "see" what it was doing. Tactile senses similar to those in the hands of an industrial worker would also be enormously beneficial. Finally, if these could be coupled with a "brain" to provide intelligent responses, numerous new robot applications would suddenly become possible. A recent study conducted at Pittsburgh's Carnegie-Mellon Robotics Center revealed that only 2 million of the 16 million production jobs in this country could be mechanized with today's mostly blind and dumb robots. But with even the most limited sight, touch, and intelligence, as many as 7 million of the tasks could be handled by the machines.

Machine Intelligence, a pioneer in robot vision systems, is located in a building that stands atop slanting concrete stilts in the heart of "Silicon Valley," a narrow crescent of land southeast of San Francisco. This morning, to keep my appointment, I have flown from Los Angeles to San Francisco and then driven a rental car into Silicon Valley, a flat, monotonous region once carpeted by groves of colorful plum trees. Today Silicon Valley is crammed with boxy, functional buildings housing the best of America's new companies that specialize in computer-based technology. In 1981, the electronics industry in the Valley had sales of $10 billion and employed 161,000 people. At least 1,500 high-technology firms have sprouted up here, many in garages, with venture capital begged and scrounged from reluctant family and friends. Many fold. Others produce—by the gross—30-year-old millionaire entrepreneurs.

Rumors of industrial spying—a few proved in court—flit across the Valley, creating subliminal feelings of suspicion. A few months before my visit, twelve representatives from Hitachi in Japan were caught trying to purchase IBM's computer secrets under the table from a sting operation set up in a phony consulting company by the FBI. Everyone I encounter seems to have his or her own version of how it happened and what it means. To allay the apparent concern of one executive, I produce a letter of agreement from my editor. "Now you can be sure that I'm a legitimate author, not a spy," I tell him. But as I begin the interview, I notice a faint flicker of mistrust on his face.

"Of course, you could be a legitimate author," he replies finally, "*and* a spy." It might be a joke. Unfortunately, the other people in his office, me included, are not laughing.

To be fair, there are lighter moments in the Valley. For instance, when I met with the president of International Machine Intelligence, Dr. Earl Sacerdoti, in his office after an earlier telephone conversation, he asks me why I look so surprised. "Somehow I had thought from your voice on the phone, that you would be... taller," I answer self-consciously, whereupon he steps impulsively onto a chair and conducts the next part of the interview while towering over me, his head barely clearing the ceiling.

In answer to a question about the importance of his work to robotics, Dr. Sacerdoti explains that today's industrial robots fill a gap between versatile human labor and hard automation—mechanisms designed for a single, specific repetitive job. With vision and other senses—and the brains to respond to what they see and feel—robots can expand their usefulness in two directions, taking over more of the jobs handled by other machines—and more of the jobs handled by human beings. However, Dr. Sacerdoti, like many of the other experts I have interviewed, is quick to point out that this will be a gradual transition. As another robot proponent observes: "By the most optimistic estimate, we may have 200,000 robots in this country by 1990—not much of a challenge to 1,000,000 workers. The displacement of workers by the farm tractor was greater than we will ever see from robots." The biggest barrier to the rapid introduction of robots is, incidentally, capital. When a factory manager installs a robot, it's not like hiring a worker. He has to pay for it up front, before it does anything useful.

Although today's robots are efficient in many situations, they require expensive items of hardware to get the objects around them into the proper position. Practical experience indicates that the cost of the required fixtures and jigs will roughly match the price of the robot itself, which ranges somewhere between $10,000 and $120,000. These heavy installation costs are necessary because robots are largely unaware of their surroundings. If an object is out of position, the robot may miss it entirely or fail to pick it up. A few centimeters of offset or misalignment can make the difference between safe handling and a damaged part—or worse, a damaged robot.

Many of the machines in today's factories are as mindless as the chilling creations in *The Stepford Wives*, a film in which the women in a suburban community are replaced by androids similar to those developed by the engineers at Disneyland.

We find it impossible to picture a human worker behaving in such a mindless manner—unless he is imitating a machine. But what is the difference between human and machinelike behavior? Clearly, a part of the distinction centers around the ability to adapt to changes in the situation. When you are driving a van or munching on a cheeseburger, you do not blindly execute a long sequence of pre-planned movements. Instead, you watch what is happening as you proceed, and make subtle but appropriate adjustments in the way you behave. This process of observation and adjustment is called *feedback control*.

The best everyday example of feedback control is a household thermostat, a device rigged with a sandwich of two different metals which expand at different rates when their temperature changes. If my thermostat is set at 69 degrees but the temperature in my house falls lower, the metal strip will increase its curvature, thus triggering a switch that causes my furnace to ignite. When the house heats up to 69 degrees—or slightly higher—the bimetallic strip flattens out again and causes the furnace to shut itself down.

The human body is a thicket of feedback control mechanisms which, in some respects, complicate its behavior and make it hard to treat when sick. Medicate it with drugs to cure an undesirable condition such as high blood pressure, and the body will gradually stop producing pressure-regulating substances of its own. Now stop taking the drug for financial or other reasons, and you may have a worse problem than you had when you started.

When you sneeze, cough, or shiver, your body is making feedback responses to your environment. Specifically, a shiver induces the consumption of more calories, thus warming your muscles. It also causes tiny hairs on your body to stand on end for better insulation. A similar thing happens when you swim or play tennis. When your body becomes oxygen-starved, it commands your lungs to take in more oxygen and your heart to beat faster to carry the oxygen-rich blood to your muscles at a more rapid rate.

The use of computers in feedback control is, of course, relatively new; but the concept itself can be traced back to antiquity. One of the earliest and most successful feedback control mechanisms, the centrifugal governor, was perfected by James Watt in 1788. His governor consisted of a vertical axle on which two crisscrossing scissorlike arms were mounted. These jointed arms carried weights so that, as the engine speed increased, they were hurled outward by centrifugal force. This produced a small radial movement which activated a mechanical linkage to close a valve, thus reducing the amount of

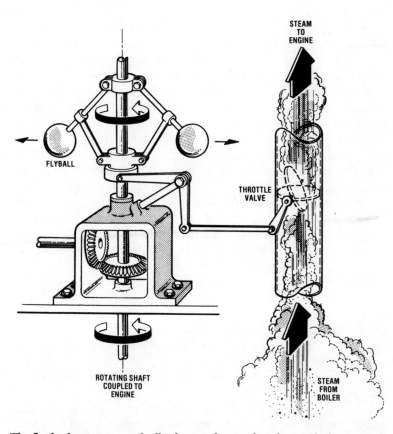

STEAM
TO
ENGINE

FLYBALL

THROTTLE
VALVE

ROTATING SHAFT
COUPLED TO
ENGINE

STEAM
FROM
BOILER

The flywheel governor uses feedback control to regulate the speed of an internal or external combustion engine. If the engine speed increases, the spinning balls swing farther outward. This causes the linkage on the right to squeeze down the throttle valve to reduce the supply of steam or fuel to the engine. An engine slowdown causes the opposite corrective action to occur. Similar feedback mechanisms are used in robots and other automatic machines.

steam being supplied to the engine. Feedback control caused Watt's steam engines to run at a more-or-less constant speed to increase their efficiency and protect them from damage should they encounter a runaway situation.

Nearly 200 years have passed since Watt invented the centrifugal governor, but with minor modifications, it is still in widespread use today. James Watt, however, was not the first to employ feedback control. For hundreds of years the Dutch have used a primitive version of the same concept to keep their windmills facing toward the wind. A small vane at right angles to the main blades causes the top of the mill to swivel so that the blades will catch the full force of the wind. The ancient Romans also utilized feedback control in the float-control valves in their plumbing systems.

Computer programs, similar to the ones that guide our interplanetary rockets, process the feedback control measurements in a modern robot. Of course, an effective feedback control mechanism must include accurate sensors to detect changes in the local environment. Many of today's robots receive information from simple detectors and switches attached to their own bodies, the assembly line, or nearby machines. But the new models will get a more complete picture of their surroundings from electronic vision and tactile sensors. A few good vision systems using television cameras are already in use. For instance, they sort tomatoes and perform inspections of pocket calculators. However, tactile sensors with reasonable resolution are working only in the laboratories. If they can be made to work well, they will be able to sense contact between tool and workpiece and detect parts misalignment. So far, even in the laboratory, they do not work very well.

When a human examines an object, he sees it with his eye and analyzes it with his brain. This suggests a simple method for giving vision to a robot: why not substitute a television camera for the eye and a computer for the brain? It's a reasonable plan; unfortunately, executing it brings unforeseen complications. For one thing, a television camera produces a prodigious amount of data—more than any small-scale computer can absorb and process in "real time." When an engineer talks about real-time processing, he means that the computer finishes its calculations so fast that the outcome of the computations can be used to influence the process being simulated. For certain situations, this may not require a very fast computer. For instance, the rescue of the *Apollo 13* astronauts which became necessary when an explosion ripped through their oxygen tanks four-fifths of the way to the moon was masterminded by computer in real time, but it required several days to accomplish. If large amounts of data must be processed quickly before the computer can act or if the data keep accumulating continuously, real-time processing may be impractical.

A single frame from a black-and-white television program contains an estimated 8 million "bits" of information. In other words, 8 million 1's and 0's would be needed to characterize the contents of the image. American television stations transmit 30 frames per second. Thus, a computer trying to analyze a complete television show in real time would be swamped by 240 million binary 1's and 0's every second—864 billion every hour. On the other hand, a typical robot "brain" can process something like 250,000 numbers per second, and its high-speed memory can typically hold about 8 million binary numbers. The difficulty of this data-storage-and-manipulation problem was brought into sharp focus in 1979 in a project headed by Dr. Hans Moravec at Stanford, who programmed a mobile robot to observe and negotiate a simple obstacle course. The machine managed to move barely 3 feet in 15 minutes!

The vision system demonstrated by Dr. Dave Milgram at Machine Intelligence keeps up with its work load by taking periodic freeze-frame "snapshots" and by strictly limiting the amount of analysis it performs. In the wrench-sorting demonstration, for instance, the computer is able to distinguish between only four objects from their silhouettes. The objects must contrast sharply with their background, and they must not overlap by more than a small amount. Sharp contrast can be achieved with ease in the laboratory; but in a factory it may be very difficult to get the proper lighting, and the objects to be manipulated may be greasy or dirty. Moreover, in today's factories parts often arrive at their work station jumbled together in a bin, so that the distinction between object and background may not be obvious to the computer. This so-called "bin stacking" problem is one of the most difficult and important now being tackled by vision researchers.

Vision systems capable of distinguishing various shades of gray would greatly increase any robot's ability to operate effectively. A television picture is divided into tiny rectangles called "pixels" (picture elements). A typical low-resolution scene can be broken down into 100,000 pixels—roughly 300 rows arranged into 300 columns. At

Machine Intelligence, each pixel is denoted by a binary 1 (white) or a binary 0 (black). There are no intermediate shades of gray. On the other hand, if each pixel were characterized by an integer between 0 and 7, for instance, eight different monochromatic shades ranging from black to white could be stored in the computer's memory and processed to extract useful information.

The use of eight shades of gray increases the computer's storage requirements by a factor of about 3, but it greatly enhances the robot's powers of discrimination. The factor-of-3 increase stems from the fact that the computer stores and processes its numbers in binary, a numeration system involving only two digits: 0 and 1. The binary numeration system uses positional notation just like our decimal number system.

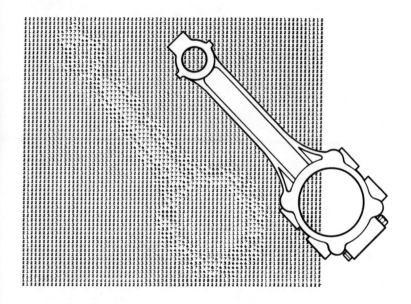

A robot looking at this connecting rod reduces the scene it sees in its television eye to an array of 100,000 pixels—tiny rectangular picture elements whose average shade of gray is represented by a number between 0 and 7. A solid-black pixel is represented by a 0; a 7 denotes one that is solid white. This array of numbers is computer-processed to help the robot recognize the connecting rod from its shape, perimeter, center of gravity, and reflectivity. Some of today's vision systems can identify a few specific objects under laboratory conditions, but they have great difficulty recognizing unfamiliar objects in the real world.

In a positional notation system, part of the value of a digit arises from its shape and part from its position relative to the other digits in the string. The number 346 is different from the number 364 even though it is made up of the same decimal digits. In our decimal number system the columns are valued as ones, tens, hundreds, thousands, and so on; the binary number system has columns (reading from right to left) valued as ones, twos, fours, eights, and so on. Thus, if we have eight shades of gray ranging from 0 to 7, we can represent them with three binary digits each as 000, 001, 010, 011, 100, 101, 110, and 111. Gray scales with as many as 256 shades are now in use; eight binary digits are required to characterize the gray-shade level of each pixel.

An ordinary television camera of the type used by commercial broadcasting stations can provide useful images to a robot. Commercial t.v. cameras are relatively inexpensive, but their slight misalignment and flicker create problems for the computer; it never knows for sure on any frame if it is analyzing precisely the same picture elements as on the frame before. A more manageable approach employs a rectangular array of light-sensitive chips similar to the ones carried by spy satellites. In an array of this type, each pixel is tended by its own tiny detector located right on the chip. This detector is switched on or off by the light illuminating it through an optical lens. This approach is accurate and reliable, but expensive.

In some simple situations, such as sorting a few simple kinds of objects on a conveyor belt, linear scanning can serve as a practical alternative. Electronic sensors are positioned in a single straight row across the conveyor, and the belt is illuminated by a thin, flat beam of light running crosswise to its direction of motion. As the belt moves, the sensors produce an instantaneous line of light that varies in intensity as it slowly scans each object. The movement of the conveyor slowly scans the light across the object. This approach minimizes data storage and analysis, but it will work only if the robot is manipulating relatively simple shapes such as wrenches or connecting rods. If the shapes are more complicated, it needs to "remember" all the measurements until they are completely analyzed. This defeats the purpose of linear scanning.

So far we have concerned ourselves with objects distinguishable by their two-dimensional silhouettes; a robot may also, however, be required to interpret three-dimensional figures. Human beings have binocular vision; our two eyes, pointed in parallel directions, view

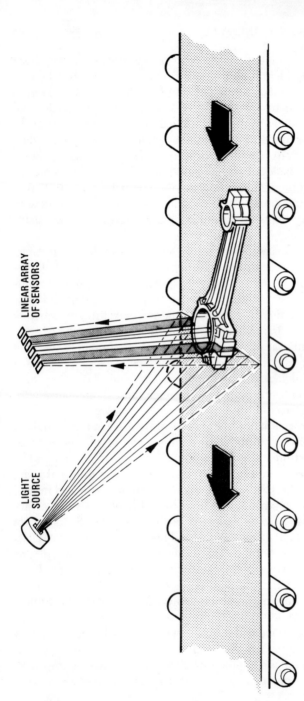

LINEAR ARRAY
OF SENSORS

LIGHT
SOURCE

A light-sensitive linear array can be used to scan the parts passing in front of it on a moving conveyor. The array is directed toward a line of light projected at an angle onto the conveyor belt. When a part blocks the light, it sees dark. If no part is present, the array sees a line of white light. With a linear array the computer deals with only 100 numbers at a time, instead of 10,000 or more that would be required for a crude two-dimensional television image of the same scene.

the same scene, but the images they register are slightly offset from each other. Subtle differences as seen from the two different vantage points provide depth clues to allow the brain to reassemble a picture of any three-dimensional objects being viewed. Unfortunately, major stumbling blocks are encountered in attempting to equip a robot with binocular vision. For one thing, it cannot always tell the difference between true edges and cast shadows. There is also the "correspondence" problem. Somehow edges and objects in the two views must be matched with each other. It sounds easy because we do it all the time with our own eyes; but for a complex scene, it can be surprisingly difficult. Moreover, there is no clear-cut way to make sure the robot has done it right.

The correspondence problem is further complicated by the fact that the various objects appear in slightly different parts of the two pictures. Moreover, a particular region in one of the pictures may be out of the field of view of the other or it may be obscured by another object. Even the most powerful computer may be unable to resolve all these difficulties satisfactorily if the scene being analyzed is subtle and complicated.

Once a robot manages to analyze a scene successfully, it is still not obvious how it should store the resulting three-dimensional objects in its memory. Some researchers employ simple geometric shapes, such as cones, pyramids, and spheres, to represent the contours of more complicated objects. For certain applications, this is a workable solution, but as science writer Paul Kinnucan points out, it is "an approach only slightly more sophisticated than representing people by stick figures."

Nevertheless, simple methods occasionally work well. Stanford University's ACRONYM vision system, for instance, can recognize a commercial jet from only three simple features: two curved lines running along the wings and a straight line on the fuselage. It works, even for oblique angles between camera and aircraft.

In addition to binocular vision, researchers are attempting to measure and characterize three-dimensional objects via two other promising methods: *range finding* and *structured light*. In range finding, the robot sends a laser beam toward a portion of the object and measures the time elapsed before it receives a reflection. A map of the entire surface of the object can be constructed by systematic scanning. Radar systems employ similar techniques with similar results.

The structured-light method entails the illumination of the scene with a specific family of light beams. The contours of the reflection provide clues concerning the shape of the object being illuminated. For instance, horizontal bars of light falling on a convex shape such as the outside of a soup bowl will be reflected as gentle, nearly parallel curves. If the same horizontal bars hit a particular angular surface they will form a distinctive chevron pattern.

Dr. Takeo Kanade at Carnegie-Mellon's Robotics Institute has devised an ingenious depth sensor based on another form of structured light. A small circle of light-emitting diodes creates a converging cone of light which comes to a point in the vicinity of the object being scanned. If the object lies at the focal point, the sensor sees a single pinpoint of light. If it is closer or farther away, however, the sensor sees a family of lights formed in a small circle. Obviously, the diameter of the circle is a measure of the error in the object's position, but at this point the situation seems ambiguous. How can the sensor determine whether the object is too close or too far away? The ambiguity is resolved by activating the light-emitting diodes one at a time in rapid sequence. Thus, the reflected lights appear to circle in a clockwise or a counterclockwise direction, depending on whether the object is on the *near* side or the *far* side of the point of convergence.

The measurements provided by a robot's vision sensors are usually analyzed by a general-purpose microcomputer like the TRS-80 or a more powerful minicomputer such as the PDP-10 manufactured by the Digital Equipment Corporation. An alternative approach now under consideration entails the use of special microprocessor chips specially designed for the purpose of analyzing vision inputs. So far, no one has built a dedicated chip of this type. But to judge from the results of similar projects in the past, dedicated chips should be considerably more efficient than a general-purpose computer.

Two researchers at Stanford University, Dr. Michael R. Lowrey and Dr. Allan Miller, have developed plans for a special-purpose vision analyzer consisting of an array of microprocessors fabricated on a single silicon wafer 2.8 inches in diameter. Unlike the sequential analysis usually employed by general-purpose computers, the individual processors on the chip will operate in parallel to analyze the light intensity of the individual pixels. Among other things, the chip will detect edges, determine robot operations, and perform correlations to determine how closely two images match. Lowrey and Miller are convinced that the mass production of their vision chip would greatly reduce the cost of robot vision systems while enhancing their sophistication. Some estimates point toward processing speeds as much as 2,500 times as fast as those achieved by a general-purpose computer.

Robots with television eyes are already beginning to reach the commercial marketplace in small numbers. Octek in Bedford, Massachusetts, has recently devised a technique for counting paper cups based on gray-scale processing. System accuracy is apparently good enough to render needless the custom of including extra cups to avoid short-counting customers. Lockheed-California is developing an automatic riveting machine for aircraft assembly using vision-guided robots to pick parts from storage racks, position them on a riveting machine, and then inspect the finished product. In Winston-Salem, North Carolina, Westinghouse will soon be forging turbine blades using sighted robots. The robots will select billets from a pallet, insert them into the furnace for heating, then place them in a swaging machine for shaping. Before sending them along the line, the robot will then inspect them to make sure they are perfectly formed.

Although the robot business as a whole is maturing, the machine vision market is still in its infancy. Industry sources estimate that revenues from vision systems amounted to only about $20 million in 1982, more than 90 percent of those sales coming from custom installations devoted to a narrow objective such as the inspection of linear welding seams. However, many insiders are convinced that the vision-systems market is about to explode. By their reckoning, sales will probably double or even triple annually during the next 4 or five years.

The sighted robots in the factory of the future may need to supplement their vision capabilities with the sense of touch. A robot that lacks tactile senses is analogous to a human who attempts to manipulate objects with numb fingers. It has no sense of the shape and position of whatever it is holding. Touch is especially important for close-up assembly work in which the workpiece may be obscured by the other parts being assembled or by the hands and arms of the robot. Other robots will need touch in order to sense their own movements during delicate operations. The ideal tactile sensor would match or exceed the responsiveness of the human hand. In addition, it should be small enough to fit on the hand of a robot, cheap enough to be widely affordable, and rugged enough for routine use in dirty and abrasive factory environments. Unfortunately, no one is even close to designing and building a system with this collection of desirable characteristics.

Recently John Purbrick of the Artificial Intelligence Laboratory at M.I.T. introduced me to some of the simplest tactile sensors now under development and some of the most sophisticated. In his laboratory, a swivel-jointed robot was executing a mechanical dance. Styrofoam padding rimmed the robot's work space, and I noticed that some of the researchers wandering around the laboratory bore suspicious-looking lumps and cuts. I was reminded of the Japanese workman at Kawasaki who had been crushed to death a year earlier by an industrial robot he so greatly admired.

In another part of the laboratory, we observed the movements of a "multi-axis force-sensor system"—a fancy name for a simple but effective device capable of sensing and measuring horizontal forces. It consists of two parallel 3-inch metal jaws, one on the left, one on the right, pointing downward. The objects it picks up are ordinary Dixie cups. Each jaw is rigged with two force sensors at different locations to measure the torques, or twisting forces, induced by the Dixie cup. The sensors are linked to a television set displaying a sketch of the left half of the robot's jaw. Whenever the robot picks up an object, a drawing of a straight, horizontal line automatically appears at the exact spot along the image of the jaw where the robot is touching the cup. The length of the line is proportional to the amount of force being exerted.

The robot has been rigged to give a lively and interesting demonstration of its limited capabilities. Whenever it picks up a single Dixie cup, a sign immediately appears on the screen: "ONE DIXIE CUP." If it is given two Dixie cups, one inside the other, the sign says instead: "MORE THAN ONE DIXIE CUP." The stiffness of the cups it is handling determines which response it will give. If a smaller Dixie cup is substituted, the sign changes to: "SMALL DIXIE CUP." The robot figures this out by measuring the distance separating its two jaws when it encounters the resistance of the cup.

"We have designed this device so that it is very efficient," Purbrick tells me. "Most units of this type close very slowly to avoid damaging the things they are picking up; but we designed this one so its jaws close rapidly. Then, when it feels the Dixie cup, it backs off a fraction of an inch and then closes in again more slowly."

At one point, the sign on the screen says "ONE DIXIE CUP" when

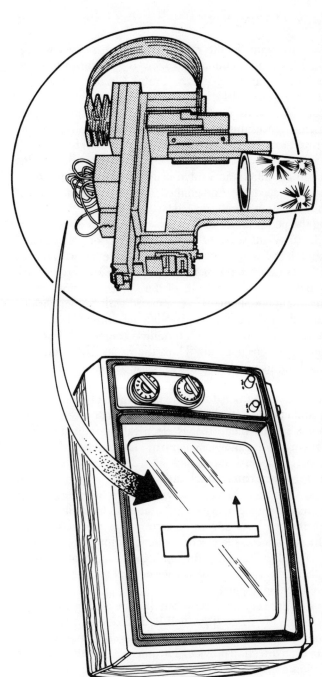

With two simple force sensors and a small computer, this M.I.T. robot distinguishes between Dixie cups of two sizes and decides if it is picking up two or more cups. Simple linear equations are solved in determining the location of the cup along the gripper and the amount of force being applied. The device also senses the size of the opening between its jaws when it first encounters resistance. The line on the television screen pinpoints the exact point where the jaw touches the paper cup; its length is proportional to the applied force.

clearly there are two cups in the robot's jaws. Here as everywhere, machines invariably malfunction when there is a visitor in the laboratory—especially if he is a dignitary. Purbrick glares at the robot for a moment with a peeved look on his face; he then glances back in my direction. "You must be more important than I thought," he says, self-consciously running his hand through his moplike hair.

Purbrick's multi-axis force-sensor system would be useful for such simple tasks as sorting bolts or ball bearings. However, he and his fellow researchers are much more interested in devising touch sensors that duplicate or exceed the fine-grained resolution of the human fingertips. They call such a sophisticated tactile sensor "artificial skin."

Duplicating the performance of human skin is not as difficult as it might seem, because our sense of touch is rather poorly developed. A square centimeter of skin on your upper arm is dotted with only a dozen distinct pressure-sensitive spots. A comparable area on the back of your hand has 30 sensitive regions of the same type, and one at the tip of your forefinger about 135. Compared with human vision, these few scattered sensors provide only crude resolution. The retina lining the human eye is covered with 6 million color-sensitive cones and 130 million light-sensitive rods. Thus, the visual sensors on your retina are something like 25,000 times as dense as the tactile sensors on your fingertip.

John Purbrick has constructed one successful type of artificial skin using straight rubber rods. Usually rubber is an insulator, but his rods are made from a special blend that is electrically conductive. The rods, 32 of them in all, are sandwiched into two layers in a crisscrossing grid resembling Huckleberry Finn's log raft. The curved surfaces of the rods in the two layers barely touch unless pressure is being applied at some point on the array to mash a pair of them together. Under pressure, the area of contact expands. This allows electricity to flow from a rod on the top level downward into one of the rods on the level below. In the process, the electricity bends through a 90-degree angle to flow parallel to the axis of the rod below. Electrical impulses flowing from the ends of the rods on the lower level tell the computer where pressure is being applied.

The rubber rods are very small now, but they are getting smaller—so small that eventually 32 of them will be laid down in two crisscrossing layers in an area of 1 square centimeter. An array with 16 rods running in each direction provides 256 different pressure-sensitive spots, a resolution comparable to that of the human fingertip.

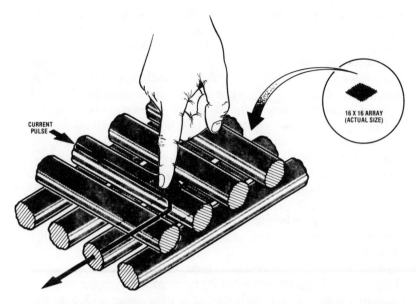

CURRENT
PULSE

16 X 16 ARRAY
(ACTUAL SIZE)

A small patch of artificial skin with 16 conductive rubber rods running in each direction is being tested by John Purbrick at the Robotics Laboratory at M.I.T. Electrical impulses are sent through each of the rods on the top layer, one at a time. If pressure is being applied at any point, the two rods at that intersection will be pushed into more intimate contact, and electricity will flow freely from the rod on the top layer into the rod below. When it is scaled down appropriately for commercial use, Purbrick's artificial skin will have a resolution roughly equivalent to that of the human fingertip.

The human nervous system detects changes in pressure continuously over the entire surface of the body. By contrast, the rows of pressure-sensitive spots on artificial skin are interrogated sequentially one after another. The computer sends electrical impulses one at a time through each of the rods in the top layer. If a force is mashing the two layers of rods together at any point, the electricity will flow downward through the intersection, bend around a right angle, and flow out the end of the rod below. By storing the outputs resulting from this systematic scanning, the computer quickly builds a crude two-dimensional picture of all the intersection points under pressure. The scanner can sweep through the entire grid 40 times a second, and in so doing it can distinguish at least 10 different levels of pressure.

Unfortunately, rubber has a tendency to "creep"; that is, the material deforms under continuous pressure. The longer you push, the flatter it becomes. This causes the tactile sensor to report stronger and stronger forces of compression even when the forces remain the same.

Artificial skin will never have tactile resolution comparable to the visual resolution of television; but it can nonetheless perform sophisticated tasks. For one thing, it can determine the difference between its robot hand suspended a thousandth of an inch above an object and one pressing firmly against it. This distinction is crucial in a factory because it could mean the difference between picking up an object and missing it entirely. Another advantage of artificial skin is that the properties we need to infer when a robot handles an object are closely akin to the properties artificial skin measures directly: shape, orientation, position. Those provided by a television system are more abstract: shading, color, reflectivity. Somehow the computer must process the properties picked up by the TV camera to infer those that are desired.

While I was in his laboratory, John Purbrick showed me some photographs of a different type of artificial skin now under development in France. The French skin covered a larger area than the specimen John had produced, and it was lying flat on a table. A pair of scissors rested on top of it, their tactile image being displayed visually on a television screen. The image was easily recognizable at a glance. There was even a noticeable gap in the image where the blades of the scissors crossed.

We also discussed another type of artificial skin, the brainchild of John's M.I.T. colleague William Daniel Hillis. The Hillis skin uses a flat sheet of silicon rubber embedded with tiny parallel conductors. This endows it with a peculiar property: it conducts electricity only in one direction. The rubber sheet is brought into contact with a printed circuit board etched with fine parallel lines running perpendicular to the conductive direction of the silicon rubber. When these two layers are brought into contact, a crisscrossing grid is produced similar to John Purbrick's artificial skin.

Scanning for the two types of skin is similar, but the Hillis version needs a porous substance to separate the two other layers of material. When pressures are low, a fine mist of nonconductive paint is a good separator. For a broader range of pressures, William Hillis has found that the best choice is nylon stockings, his personal favorite being L'eggs extra-sheer panty hose. As many as 2,500 pressure-sensitive

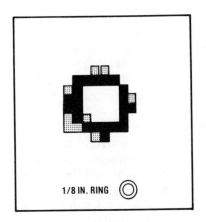

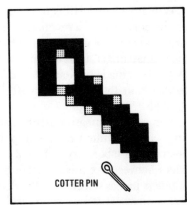

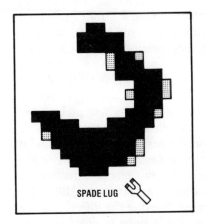

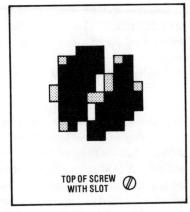

M.I.T. researcher William Daniel Hillis tested his artificial skin to see if it could distinguish between six small metal fasteners. These tactile images show what the robot sensed when it pressed its skin-covered finger against four of the fasteners. The sketch below each tactile image represents the actual size of each object. Although these tactile images may seem a little crude, the computer was correct in all six identifications.

intersections per square centimeter are possible, enough to provide 20 times the resolution of human fingertips.

William Daniel Hillis has mounted a sample of his artificial skin on the curved tip of a mechanical finger with roughly the same shape, size, and range of movement as the forefinger of a human adult. Like the human finger, it is equipped with three swiveling joints, controlled by tendons made of Kevlar, a space-age plastic with a bending radius tighter than that of stainless steel and a nearly comparable tensile strength.

The pressure measurements made by the skin-covered mechanical finger are fed into a microcomputer for evaluation. Hillis has demonstrated in laboratory tests that the finger can distinguish the differences between six metal fasteners each less than ½ inch long. The fasteners he has selected for the demonstration include small washers, cotter pins, set screws, and spade lugs. The finger determines the overall shape of the object from the ratio of its length to width, and its inherent stability is checked by testing to see if it rolls freely on a smooth surface. The device also counts holes and bumps, and pinpoints their locations, by analyzing local pressure anomalies on the surface.

Usually a robot rigged with a vision sensor gathers all the data it needs first, then analyzes it. However, the Hillis tactile finger employs a completely different approach. First it makes a few preliminary measurements so that it can come up with an educated guess as to the identity of the object. Then, on the basis of what it decides, it orders a new battery of tests to verify or negate its preliminary hypothesis. A gradual, stepwise refinement of this process usually leads toward the correct identity of the object. According to Hillis, his stepwise method is appropriate because "moving the finger...is the best way to collect meaningful data. But in order to decide how to move the finger, the program must have some expectation of what object it is feeling." He goes on to add with scarcely concealed pride that "if the image...is not satisfactory, it is possible to move the finger and [create] another—we do not have to rely on first impressions."

Of course, anyone who has ever handled an ice cube or a thistle realizes that human skin is responsive to external stimuli other than pressure. In particular, it is sensitive to remarkably small variations in temperature and texture. Tests in the laboratory have shown that the fingers of a trained inspector can detect a grease coating only one molecule thick. Robots will probably never be competitive with such a skilled individual, but they may be able to use an ordinary phonograph needle to distinguish gross differences in texture between materials such as paper and glass. The needle is slowly scraped across the surface and its vibrational patterns are analyzed by a computer. The temperature of an object, such as a snowball or a heated rivet, can be determined by a thermocouple consisting of two intertwined wires made of certain dissimilar metals such as copper and iron. When the thermocouple is heated, a small electrical current is induced. This current can drive a variety of laboratory instruments, whose outputs are proportional to the temperature of the object.

Even when wood and steel are at the same temperature, steel feels cooler to the touch. This stems from the fact that steel is a superior conductor, so that it more quickly carries heat away from the body. A tiny resistance heater sandwiched between two thermocouples should be able to measure subtle differences in thermal conductivity between various materials.

When artificial skin and other tactile sensors become commonplace, researchers should be able to build tactile telephones to allow people to hold hands over continent-wide distances. If you are separated from your loved ones, you will be able to slip your hands into glovelike devices and squeeze and caress lovers and relatives. "Reach out and touch someone" will become more than an advertising slogan. Realistic feedback between the parties involved will make this a mutually rewarding experience. It may well become one of the most personal and satisfying spin-offs of the robot revolution.

CHAPTER 5

MACHINES "WHO" THINK?

In 1964 at Stanford University's Artificial Intelligence Laboratory, Dr. John McCarthy put together the plans for a powerful new robot. It was to include binocular vision, language-understanding capabilities, and planning and control hardware—everything it would need, he believed, to assemble from scratch a Heathkit color television set. Unfortunately, John McCarthy's dreams outstripped reality by a yawning margin. This is how Victor Scheinman, a young member of the Stanford staff, tells of their failure to build such a robot:

> In 1965 we bought the Heathkit television set. In 1966 the Heathkit color television got assembled by a few students. About 1975 the Heathkit color television finally gave up the ghost, having operated satisfactorily for ten years. It now sits in a dark closet.

Although his remarks may seem a bit negative, Victor Scheinman is not pessimistic about robot technology; he is one of its most enthusiastic practitioners. Moreover, he is convinced that in the foreseeable future, Dr. McCarthy's dream will be realized—in a curious sort of way: "I personally believe that there will come a day when (a robot) will be able to assemble the Heathkit television set," he stated in a recent interview; "but by the time (it is available), Heathkit will have . . . a model that all you have to do is . . . get it out of the cardboard box and plug in a single chip."

Giving a robot the ability to assemble a complicated television set without human assistance will require fundamental breakthroughs in *artificial intelligence*—an intriguing, highly mathematical branch of technology. Since the 1930s debates have been raging as to whether or not a machine could ever exhibit intelligence of the type that seems so natural to human beings. Part of the difficulty stems from the fact that it is so tricky to formulate a workable definition of intelligence. Most experts agree that it involves such stringy and nebulous concepts as the ability to recognize subtle patterns, to deal with abstract symbols, and to learn from past experiences. Fortunately, M.I.T. Professor Marvin Minsky has found a way out of this apparently fruitless argument. He has proposed that we sidestep the issue by defining *artificial* intelligence as "The science of making machines do things that would require intelligence if done by men." In Dr. Minsky's view, for instance, a machine that plays a winning game of chess or translates a novel from one language to another is exhibiting artificial intelligence even if it does these things by trickery or brute force, as opposed to more elegant humanlike thought processes.

A machine that could successfully mimic even simple human thinking would be enormously helpful in the office or in the factory. For instance, a robot with artificial intelligence could, like its human counterpart, respond appropriately if it encountered ill-fitting or defective parts, or other unexpected anomalies. Other promising applications for thinking machines include seafloor mining of manganese nodules and the repair of orbiting satellites with spacefaring robots. For at least 10 years, teams of civilian and military researchers have been studying the design and operation of maintenance robots for use in outer space. Such a machine would rendezvous with a disabled satellite, hook on to it, then perform a series of diagnostic tests to determine the fault in its operation. The robot would either make the necessary repairs on the spot or carry the satellite back to the space shuttle, where it would be fixed by the astronauts or returned to a repair station on earth.

Military research teams are also studying the possibility of using unmanned but intelligent fighter aircraft and unmanned robot tanks to be interspersed with manned tanks in massive military maneuvers. Teleoperator control would be used to some extent, but the tanks would also be equipped with sensors and on-board computers to provide responsive, autonomous operation.

Of course, many of today's most promising and successful applications of artificial intelligence do not involve robots at all. These include computerized medical diagnoses, automatic interpretations of mineral-exploration data, and the design of "user-friendly" computers that prompt and cajole the user into their efficient operation. It is hoped that in the long run, the techniques learned in carrying out these projects will help in the development of cheap but intelligent industrial robots.

As a full-blown discipline, artificial intelligence has existed for only a decade or two; but almost from its infancy it developed a terrible reputation among other scientists, especially those who controlled research purse strings. In part, these negative reactions were a quite understandable response to the often outlandish predictions made by certain practitioners in the field, who frequently followed up with widely publicized failures.

In 1968, Marvin Minsky himself put together a wildly optimistic prediction of the future of artificial intelligence. In an article published in *Science Journal,* he stated that

> Today, machines solve problems according to the principles we build into them. Before long, we may learn how to set them to work upon the very special problem of improving their capacity to solve problems. Once a certain threshold is passed, this could lead to a spiral of acceleration and it may be hard to perfect a reliable "governor" to restrain it.

Dr. Minsky was not the first overly enthusiastic advocate of machine intelligence. In 1957 another talented researcher, Dr. Herbert Simon, convinced himself that computers can do anything people can do, only better. Soon after he coded a computer program that was heralded in the popular press as duplicating human thought processes, he turned his attention toward the ultimate limits of artificial intelligence:

> It is not my aim to surprise or shock you... But the simplest way I can summarize it is to say that there are now in the world machines that think,... learn, and... create. Moreover, their ability to do these things is going to increase rapidly until—in the visible future—the range of

problems they can handle will be coextensive with the range to which the human mind has been applied.

The "machines" he was referring to were digital computers, and their ability to "think, . . . learn, and . . . create" was strictly subject to interpretation. At the time there were only a handful of computers in use, and very few of them did anything remotely simulating human thought processes. The last part of his statement was, indeed, a brave, farsighted prophecy. So brave, so farsighted, that the "visible future" of total problem solving to which he refers never seems to get appreciably closer. One is reminded of the faithful old Trotskyite who said of his hero: "Proof of Trotsky's farsightedness is that none of his predictions have come true yet."

Of course, even in those early days there were critics of artificial intelligence, including Dr. Hubert Dreyfus, who wrote a clever and convincing book titled *What Computers Can't Do*. It opens with a summary of some of the more jarring failures of the best-known researchers in the field. Dr. Dreyfus is especially suspicious of self-serving claims. As he puts it, "The value of a program is often inversely proportional to its programmer's promises and publicity."

Another early pioneer, Dr. Joseph Weitzenbaum, has often spoken out against the excesses of the experts in computer programming and artificial intelligence. In his popular book *Computer Power and Human Reason*, Dr. Weitzenbaum argues that there are some assignments we should avoid computerizing even if the computer could, in principle, handle them efficiently. He also bemoans the fact that most of the important decisions in the modern world are arrived at by the juggling of numbers and statistics. A century ago, intelligent people were convinced that education should involve broad-ranging cultural experiences in addition to the study of those things we can quantify. Today, unfortunately, culture is often regarded as highbrow entertainment—not as a means of approaching insight and truth, and certainly not as a way of achieving mastery over our everyday affairs.

In November of 1982, I interviewed Dr. Weitzenbaum in his office at M.I.T. His is a gaunt face dominated by big, intense eyes tinted with a trace of sadness. When he speaks, he radiates a feeling of soft Southern charm. News of the Palestinian massacre in Lebanon had just leaked out and as we talked, he was using a computer terminal in his office to exchange short typewritten messages detailing his humanitarian response to the tragedy with a colleague in Australia. It pleased him to be harnessing computer technology to make contact with someone so far away. When the clattering stopped, I asked him his opinion on the probable effects of automation and artificial intelligence on America's workers. After a thoughtful pause, he began to paint a picture of the present situation the way he perceived it, and the future situation the way he hoped it would turn out to be: "For three hundred years there have been direct ties between working and eating. In the past, this has been necessary, when there was not enough wealth to go around. But now that there is an abundance, there is no reason to punish a person who isn't working."

He realized, of course, that we would face a difficult period of transition before we could adapt our thinking to this magnanimous approach. This led him to an interesting parallel: "We have succeeded in separating *sex* and *reproduction*—something that would have been inconceivable a hundred years ago. We got through that one—with some difficulty. Now we need to do the same thing with *work* and *survival*."

The book *Computer Power and Human Reason* was inspired by a series of incidents that occurred many years ago when Dr. Weitzenbaum developed a special computer program called "ELIZA." It was a cleverly designed routine that carried on "conversations" with people in which it mimicked the verbal responses of a nondirective Rogerian psychotherapist. ELIZA was a delightful program to operate, and occasionally it seemed impressively intelligent. In reality, of course, it had no understanding of the typed "conversation." Instead, it was programmed to recognize a few common English words and parrot back an appropriate question or response. If it encountered a sentence containing a key word like "father" or "mother," it might reply: "Tell me more about your family." If it got stuck, it would make a noncommittal reply like "Go on" or "What does that suggest to you?"

In Weitzenbaum's opinion, ELIZA was a simpleminded bag of tricks with no capabilities even remotely resembling human intelligence. But it was an easy program to demonstrate to the uninitiated, and soon it became widely known on the campus at M.I.T. Many people, even those who should have known better, began to believe in the therapeutic powers of ELIZA. This shocked and baffled Joseph Weitzenbaum. "I was startled to see how quickly and how very deeply people conversing with ELIZA became emotionally involved with the computer and how unequivocally they anthropomorphized it. Once my secretary, who had watched me work on the program for many months and therefore surely knew it to be merely a computer program, started conversing with it. After only a few interchanges with it, she asked me to leave the room."

The apparent willingness, even eagerness, of professionals in the psychiatric community to use the program on mentally disturbed patients left him even more shocked and disoriented. "What must a psychiatrist who makes such a suggestion think he is doing while treating a patient, that he can view the simplest mechanical parody of a simple interviewing technique as having captured anything of the essence of a human encounter?"

After mulling over these and similar philosophical questions concerning people's curious responses to their electronic servants, Dr. Weitzenbaum decided to write a book which was eventually titled *Computer Power and Human Reason: From Judgment to Calculation*. In it he maintained that the human brain is more than a mere "meat machine." This term was earlier coined by Marvin Minsky to underscore his belief that the human brain, like a computer, is made of physical components and is therefore in no meaningful sense a special or mystical mechanism. Without tackling this belief head on, Dr. Weitzenbaum argues that there are some humanistic undertakings—such as psychotherapy and criminal justice—which we should never turn over to our computers, regardless of how fairly, efficiently, and intelligently computers might be able to handle them.

Much of the early research in artificial intelligence was highly intellectual and entirely impractical. But in the 1970s, after a salvo of overblown claims, a number of devastating failures, and a punishing avalanche of criticism, the emphasis began to change. Many experts gradually abandoned the esoteric methods they had been using and instead adopted a new survival strategy in which they emphasized the useful end results of their work. Promising new applications generated tingling enthusiasm. These included training robots and other machines to interact with the real world, creating computer terminals that were much easier for ordinary people to use, and developing "expert systems" in which researchers picked the brains of knowledgeable individuals, then used the computer to duplicate their decision-making techniques.

Many of the most spectacular applications of artificial intelligence have been achieved in game-playing computers. Some early researchers, for instance, programmed their machines to play tic-tac-toe—a simple rainy-day children's game in which two players alternately place X's and O's in a three-by-three grid. The first player to get three of these symbols in a row—horizontally, vertically, or diagonally—wins the game. Once the program is coded properly, the computer never loses; at worst, the game ends in a draw.

A tic-tac-toe program is relatively easy to develop. In fact, the game is so simple that two computer experts in the 19th century, Charles Babbage and Ada Lovelace, briefly considered building a tic-tac-toe machine in order to raise money to finance further work on the machine they called the Analytical Engine. They envisioned a "grand tour" of Europe in which they would charge admission to enthusiastic swarms of curious spectators. Unfortunately, their studies showed that the only exhibit of a similar nature that had ever brought in the kind of money they needed was P. T. Barnum's General Tom Thumb. Since there was no obvious way to build a synthetic midget, Charles and Ada sadly abandoned their idea. Soon, however, their fertile minds had devised a "foolproof" method for winning money on horse races—a notion that turned out a complete disaster. Twice Lady Lovelace had to pawn her jewels to cover her gambling debts, and a few years later she summoned Charles Babbage to her deathbed to give him last-minute instructions for paying off a particularly obnoxious loan shark. Having lost his favorite gambling companion, Babbage never pursued the idea any further.

One method of programming a computer to win at tic-tac-toe consists of arranging the moves in game-tree fashion. The branches of the game tree represent every possible legal move. For instance, the first branch of the tree goes off in three directions because there are three different moves the first player can make: (a) he can put his X in the center square, (2) he can put it in a corner, or (3) he can put it in the middle square along one side of the grid. Depending on what the first player does, the second player has either two or five choices. Thus it turns out that there are a total of twelve branches at the second level of the game tree, which continues to branch as play continues. Once the game tree is completed, all the winning strategies can be traced through its branches. The complete game tree for tic-tac-toe involves a total of about 500 branches—a number that can be managed with ease by a computer.

Why don't we adapt a similar approach in order to devise a foolproof strategy for winning at checkers and chess? Unfortunately, the complete game tree for checkers involves 10^{40}, or

10,000,000,000,000,000,000,000,000,000,000,000,000 possible moves. Even if we could use a computer to evaluate a new branch of the tree every one-millionth of a second, it would still require 300,000,000,000,000,000,000,000,000,000 years to construct the entire game tree. By the time the computer was ready to play, there would not be an opponent left to challenge it—except maybe another computer.

Chess is considerably more complicated than checkers. In the 1960s, computer expert Dr. Arthur Samuel estimated that a complete game tree for chess would involve 10^{120}, or 1,000,000,000,000,000,000,000, 000, 000, 000, 000, 000, 000, 000, 000, 000, 000, 000, 000, 000, 000, 000, 000, 000, 000, 000, 000, 000, 000, 000, 000, 000, 000, 000,000,000,000,000,000 possible moves.

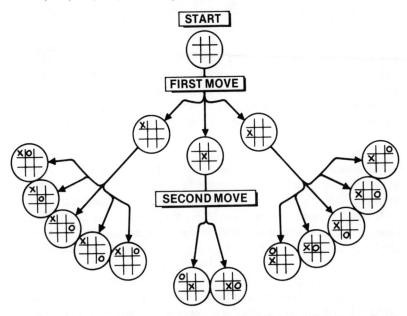

Tic-tac-toe is a simple rainy-day children's game for two contestants who alternately place X's and O's in a 3-by-3 rectangular grid. The first player who manages to get three of his symbols in a row wins the game. One method for developing a foolproof winning strategy is to arrange all the possible moves in game-tree fashion, each permissible move being represented by one branch of the tree. Once this is done, winning sequences of moves become apparent at a glance. Only a small portion of the game tree is shown in this diagram; in totality it would involve about 500 branches.

Fortunately, the experts who program computers to play checkers and chess do not find it necessary to examine all the branches of their game trees. Instead, special methods are available for "pruning" most of the branches from the tree. Moreover, the computer does not simulate the game in its entirety all the way to the end. It plans ahead only five or six moves. As it plays, it jockeys for a commanding position and tries to make profitable exchanges of pieces. The methods employed by the computer are similar to the ones used by a chess master in tournament play; but there is a crucial difference: the chess master is much better at determining what is *important* in any given situation. Those who have played chess against a computer point out that it is not a very satisfying experience. The computer never develops a grand overall strategy in the game; at first it seems to behave in a rather random fashion. But eventually, the computer's hapless opponent realizes that he is being nibbled to death by the relentless machine.

CHESS 4.6, a chess-playing program written by a group of experts at Northwestern University, has been shown in competition to play at the Master's level. This means that it is skillful enough to beat approximately 90 percent of all the chess players in the world who take the game seriously enough to be rated. Although chess research creates enthusiasm in some parts of the artificial-intelligence community, no major conceptual breakthroughs have occurred in the past few years. Better hardware and slight improvements in the programs are producing only small gains in the computer's level of play. And despite these gradual improvements, by the standards of the data-processing industry both the hardware and the software used in playing chess employ routine technology. Nevertheless, in 1982 when Ken Thompson of Bell Labs was about to board a plane bound for Moscow with his friend "Belle," a chess-playing computer, he and his machine were apprehended by officials of the Reagan Administration who feared the computer might give away national-security secrets, even though Thompson insisted that Belle's inner workings were designed specifically for playing chess. "The only way Belle could be used militarily would be to drop it out of an airplane," Thompson told a reporter. "You might kill somebody that way."

Actually, by tournament standards Belle did not even play chess very well. All the computers at the tournament were, in fact, soundly trounced by their expert opponents. Computers play the game so predictably that more versatile human players can easily capitalize on any weakness they may have. At Moscow, for instance, one computer made a terrible blunder on its fourteenth move, then went on to a humiliating defeat. Later, when another opponent played a match against the same machine, he led it through a duplicate sequence of moves, whereupon it nonchalantly made the same blunder again. However, even if they are only marginally impressive, chess programs do represent one of the first commercially successful applications of artificial intelligence. At least two of them have grossed more than $1 million each from retail sales to chess enthusiasts.

Less profitable, but much more impressive, results have been achieved by other game-playing computers. Poker programs, for instance, can defeat expert poker players—which is surprising, because the strategy of an expert focuses upon the outcome of the entire session of play, not just the piecemeal outcomes of the individual hands. So far, however, the most spectacular human defeat came in another game, backgammon—a game that supposedly requires a high degree of intelligence, at least among human competitors.

The August 1980 issue of *Scientific American* carried this terse announcement written by computer expert Hans Berliner: "Last July my backgammon-playing computer program BKG 9.8 defeated the world champion, Luigi Villa of Italy, by a score of 7 to 1 in a $5,000 winner-take-all match at Monte Carlo."

Berliner, who had once won the correspondence chess championship of the United States, went on to explain that "Unlike the best programs for playing chess, BKG 9.8 does well more by positional judgment than by brute calculation. This means that it plays backgammon much as human experts do." Although the match was played by Berliner's "Gammonoid" robot at Monte Carlo, the PDP-10 computer doing the calculations was located thousands of miles away at Carnegie-Mellon University in Pittsburgh. Robot and computer conversed by means of a communication satellite. At the beginning of the match, Gammonoid was scheduled to propel himself onto the stage as the orchestra played a rousing rendition of the theme from *Star Wars*. Unfortunately, the robot was not accustomed to performing in public, and he became so excited he got himself tangled in the curtain. A quick-witted stagehand rushed to the rescue.

Although Gammonoid was an impressively intelligent machine, it was not much to look at, nor was it very well coordinated. In a telephone interview, Hans Berliner characterized his bright little robot as being "similar to department-store models." However, to be entirely fair, Gammonoid was mobile and could "turn, move forward and backward—and rotate his arm." A hole in his stomach held a cathode-ray tube display and a speaker through which the robot could "talk" and be heard by spectators. He was rigged to obey radio commands to a limited extent, but he was unable to move the pieces on the backgammon board. Instead, his human assistant scanned the electronic display in the robot's chest and made the moves in Gammonoid's name.

The organizers of the backgammon convention at Monte Carlo had adopted Gammonoid as the official symbol of their tournament. They put his picture on all their publicity releases, and their trophies were decorated with small robot emblems. However, past experiences had apparently shown that humans were superior to backgammon-playing computers. For this reason, very few of the spectators expected more than a passable showing from the clumsy little machine.

The game of backgammon involves a combination of luck and skill. Consequently, when Gammonoid was the victor, Hans Berliner could at least make an attempt to console the machine's human opponent whose spirit was crushed by his clear-cut defeat. "I told him I was sorry it had happened," said Berliner in an interview following the match, "and that we both knew he was really the better player." Experts who saw the match in person and on television do not necessarily agree. They are convinced that Gammonoid was unusually lucky in getting good rolls of the dice; however, they also point out that the robot capitalized skillfully on his good fortune.

Game-playing programs are enjoyable and instructive; but the biggest profits from future applications of artificial intelligence are more likely to come from *man–machine interfaces* and *pattern recognition*. Man–machine-interface problems deal broadly with attempts to make computers "user-friendly" to inexperienced individuals. A user-friendly computer is able to "converse" with the user in his or her own natural language—or a slight variant of it—and respond automatically in powerful and appropriate ways. Computers rigged for pattern recognition can spot meaningful, but often obscure, patterns in a large, complicated array of data. Promising applications include routines that can search out special branching tracks on photographs taken of subatomic-particle collisions in particle accelerators such as cyclotrons and betatrons.

On both sides of the Pacific, "expert systems" are becoming the hottest new arena of competition. In an expert system, a team of researchers attempts to master, with the help of the computer, a small, well-defined specialty such as the treatment of bone cancer or the location of offshore oil deposits. For months, team members interview the experts in an attempt to discover the important protocols (rules of thumb) they use in doing their jobs successfully. Often the experts themselves have only a vague understanding of the techniques they actually use. In some cases, the research team concludes that their "expertise" is largely a myth.

To date, more than fifty expert systems have been constructed. One of the most successful is MYCIN, a computerized routine that diagnoses bacterial blood infections from standard medical symptoms. It also suggests the proper course of therapy using, principally, antibiotic drugs. MYCIN was developed by teasing out more than 500 "production rules." Typical samples go something like this:

> If the patient is black, Asian, or Indian, and the infection is fungal, then rule out cryptococcus as the infection.
> If the whites of the patient's eyes are yellow, then he has a buildup of bile pigments in his body.

With these rules of inference strung together into a logical, interacting framework, the computer becomes an untiring assistant to the physician, who is becoming increasingly overwhelmed by the complexities of modern medicine. One estimate indicates that today's M.D. requires access to 1 million facts to practice internal medicine— 2 million if medical subspecialties are included.

MYCIN helps cut through the complexity, but it applies to a rather narrow class of diseases. A new program called CADUCEUS is being designed for much broader applicability. CADUCEUS is named after Hermes' serpent-entwined staff, the traditional symbol of the medical profession. With great speed and accuracy, it sifts through its extensive knowledge of nearly 600 diseases and 4,000 medical symptoms. Its files are not yet complete; but in blind trials involving only the diseases it now understands, the diagnostic skills of CADUCEUS compare favorably with those of a cross section of practicing physicians. So far, however, it cannot match the capabilities of clinical specialists when they are working in their own fields. For the moment, the developers of CADUCEUS consider it to be experimental. According to Dr. Jack Myers of the University of Pittsburgh's Decision Systems Laboratory: "It will be another five to ten years before the system is perfected and most physicians gain access to the program."

The knowledge engineers who are attempting to develop expert systems have, so far, managed to elicit the cooperation of the experts they have been interviewing, but it has not been a very easy task. Part of the problem is that the experts are not well motivated to give their full cooperation. After all, they are being asked to give up a lifetime of hard-won expertise and to summarize it in a set of rules so precise and clear that it can be programmed into a machine. Most well-known experts can think of better ways to use their time. Theirs is precisely the sort of information and knowledge that society rewards when it is presented in technical papers, textbooks, and television interviews. It is difficult to think of many convincing reasons why they should dispense it for a small one-time fee. Moreover, it is not always clear how to develop a set of simple rules to perform most tasks. What are the rules for swimming? For wine tasting? For giving a persuasive presentation to an unruly audience? For handling a tragedy in the family? There may be rules for these activities, but if there are, they must be terribly obscure.

A new diagnostic program that is in some respects similar to CA-DUCEUS is presently being developed in England. It uses classical medical symptoms to diagnose the causes of acute abdominal pain. Blind trials at one hospital demonstrated that if it had been used in clinical practice, fewer unnecessary operations would have occurred, and fewer surgeries would have been delayed in cases of genuine appendicitis. Experimental computer programs based on the same general principles are being used to diagnose congenital heart defects and to identify mental patients who are likely to attempt suicide. Another, called ONCASYN, which was extremely difficult to program, helps doctors develop drug-therapy protocols for victims of Hodgkin's disease. ONCASYN was programmed for the Cancer Clinic at Stanford University after researchers discovered that the drug treatment of cancer patients often becomes so overpoweringly complicated that even highly trained specialists can make serious procedural errors. Blind trials have demonstrated that ONCASYN develops protocols which compare favorably with those produced by human experts.

Many expert systems employ "fuzzy thinking." This means that they manage to develop a useful line of reasoning based on incomplete or uncertain information. The need for decision making based on sloppy inputs is a common dilemma faced by the parents of teenagers as well as politicians and military commanders. Until recently, however, it was a problem seldom tackled by computer programmers.

When the user supplies information to an expert system that engages in fuzzy thinking, he specifies, if possible, his confidence in how accurate and reliable he believes the data to be. This technique has been especially valuable in the development of the "Prospector" program, an expert system that predicts the likelihood of locating economically attractive mineral deposits in a particular area. Prospector uses data entered on geological maps or obtained through a dialogue with the user. When the program has processed the data, it produces full-color contour maps that estimate the probability of finding ores at various levels of concentration. In 1981, Prospector reportedly located a new molybdenum deposit in Canada worth millions of dollars. It has also been used to locate promising copper deposits in the United States. From time to time rumors have spread concerning other successful applications. Unfortunately, the mineral industry is very secretive, so that the authenticity of these stories is difficult to verify.

Expert systems can be extremely effective for limited applications, but they have a tendency to break down if the problem becomes too broad-ranging. "What scares us about all the hype surrounding expert systems is that they are very brittle," explains John Seeley Brown, director of the Cognitive and Instructional Sciences Group at Xerox. "As soon as you go over the boundary of what they were designed to do, they collapse into a quivering heap."

By contrast, human experts do not seem to experience nearly the same level of difficulty when they are assigned to work on an unfamiliar project, provided it bears some relationship to their usual expertise. Apparently, the experts can fall back on human judgment and their overall knowledge of the situation. Of course, with careful reprogramming, some of today's artificial-intelligence programs can be adapted for use in applications other than the ones for which they were originally designed. The basic structure of the routine remains the same, but modifications are made to its inputs and a few of its commands. The blood-infection program MYCIN, for example, has been modified by researchers at Stanford University and IBM to diagnose malfunctions in magnetic disk drives.

"Deep knowledge" systems represent another way of broadening the applicability and flexibility of artificial-intelligence routines. In a deep-knowledge system, the programmer tries to look behind the simple rules of thumb used in a program like MYCIN or Prospector. His aim is to get at the memories, scientific theories, and mental models that allow the experts to develop effective protocols for their work. No one knows how it will turn out, but researchers are hoping this approach will produce more generally applicable programs than the simpler rule-based systems.

Most of today's experts in artificial intelligence are directing their efforts toward practical assignments. Only a few of them are interested in the broader philosophical issue of whether or not a machine can think. In 1936, this question was pondered at length by Alan Turing, a gifted British mathematician. Turing devised a special test intended to reveal whether or not a particular machine is in fact intelligent. In his scheme, a human interrogator would be seated in a room with two teleprinter terminals: one connected to an intelligent human subject, the other connected to a computer. The interrogator would be allowed to pose a series of questions on any desired subjects by typing them on the two teleprinters. In Turing's opinion, if the human interrogator could not distinguish which teleprinter was connected to the computer, and which was connected to the human being—on the basis of their typed replies—he would be forced to the conclusion that the computer was an intelligent entity.

This ingeniously contrived test is essentially the same one we use by instinct when we attempt to determine if a new acquaintance is an intelligent person: we fire a few questions at him to see if his replies indicate the capacity for rational thought.

Alan Turing, who believed that a machine would probably pass his test by the year 2000, put together, perhaps too fastidiously, the following series of sample questions and answers. It is interesting to note that the computer commits an error in calculation, perhaps in an attempt to deceive the interrogator.

> QUESTION: Please write me a sonnet on the subject of the Fourth Bridge.
> ANSWER: Count me out on this one. I never could write poetry.
> QUESTION: Add 34957 to 70764.
> ANSWER: (PAUSE ABOUT 30 SECONDS AND THEN GIVE AN ANSWER.) 105621.
> QUESTION: Do you play chess?
> ANSWER: Yes.
> QUESTION: I have K at my K1, and no other pieces. You have only K at K6 and R at R1. It is your move. What do you play?
> ANSWER: (AFTER A PAUSE OF 15 SECONDS.) R—R8. Mate.

These questions and answers are typical of the ones proposed by the students in my Computer Science classes at U.S.C. Fortunately,

Michael Rogers, in his novel *Silicon Valley*, has provided us with a much more creative sequence. In his account, a half-dozen celebrities are allowed to question man and machine. The replies are returned by a voice synthesizer named SOCRATES that accurately mimics the voice of a young woman—regardless of whether the reply is coming from the person or the computer. As we enter the story, the test is just about to begin:

> Bettina Williams the graying television personality was the first to speak. "Good afternoon, SOCRATES," she said.
> "It is a good afternoon," SOCRATES said.
> Bettina Williams leaned over her microphone. "Why is it a good afternoon? Because you think you'll pass this test?"
> ... "No," SOCRATES said. "I was talking about the weather."
> The members of the panel looked at each other for a moment. Bettina Williams made several notes, then cleared her throat. "Why," she asked, "do people go to war against each other?"
> ... "People go to war," SOCRATES said, "because they haven't considered other solutions."
> "Like what solutions?" Bettina asked.
> "You're the human. It's up to you."
> There was a brief flurry of laughter in the gallery.
> "Does that mean you're not human?"
> "I'm not supposed to tell you that."

The questioning continues for several minutes in the same vein, with SOCRATES giving an occasional sassy reply, which invariably triggers hearty laughter from the spectators in the gallery. Later in the story, an Argentinean poet gets his first crack at the machine:

> "SOCRATES," he said, raising one hand, "let me ask you this. Suppose you met a girl in a café, and she asked you to come home with her. Would you?"
> ... "What kind of a girl is this?"
> The poet gazed at the ceiling of the chamber for a moment, and the television cameras moved closer. "She is tall, with violet eyes and velvet skin. She is very special."
> "Would it be my home or her home?"

After discussing Turing's test at length with my students over several semesters, I have concluded that an unusually promising way to evaluate the computer's powers would be to ask it to interpret the meanings of a series of personalized license plates. A personalized license plate can include as many as seven members and letters in essentially any sequence chosen, for a fee, by the owner of the car. Many of the ones in use contain clever but cryptic messages.

In order to pass a license-plate test, the computer would have to exhibit specific real-world knowledge on a broad range of subjects. Moreover, it would be required to decode an unfamiliar "language" that its programmers would be unable to decipher for it in advance. For instance, if a personalized license plate reads "CMY MG," the computer would have to deduce that in special situations, the letter "C" can be interpreted as "see" and that a blank space is to be supplied by the reader between the "C" and the next two letters, "MY." (Only one blank space is permitted in a personalized license plate.) It would also have to determine that the symbols "M" and "G" written side by side can denote a particularly expensive and highly admired automobile. Finally, and most important, it would have to figure out that although human beings are largely indifferent to most everyday objects, many are strangely proud of the family automobile—so proud that $50 seems like a reasonable fee for adorning it with a plea for special attention. It is precisely this kind of specialized real-world knowledge which could constitute a realistic challenge to the powers of a computer that is attempting to pass the Turing test.

Alan Turing was an Englishman, but in recent years American experts have been preeminent in the many practical applications of artificial intelligence. However, if the Japanese have their way, that preeminence will vanish during the next twenty years. The Japanese Government is officially encouraging work on a broad-ranging artificial-intelligence project it calls the "Fifth Generation Computer." A total of $44.5 million has been budgeted through 1985 for fifth-generation-computer research, and about ten times that expenditure level is planned over the next decade, in addition to comparable private investments by Japanese companies. After years of making small but profitable improvements in consumer products from around the world, the Japanese are very proud of their attempts to tackle a major effort in advanced research. "This project is the Space Shuttle in the world of knowledge," explains Dr. Tohru Moto-oka, a professor at the University of Tokyo. Dr. Moto-oka chaired a recent conference on fifth-generation computer technology. It was attended by a number of Western observers who had decidedly mixed emotions on the machine's practicality.

The Japanese computer fifth-generation will feature extensive non-numeric processing capabilities. This means that its inputs will include graphs and pictures as well as numbers and words. The machine will communicate with its programmers and its users with ordinary sentences from English and Japanese; a vocabulary of 10,000 words is being projected by 1990. User-friendliness, especially for nonprogrammers, is also an overriding goal of the machine's designers: "Fifth-generation computers will be as easy to use as telephones," claims one Kyoto University professor. The Fifth Generation Computer will incorporate extremely efficient programming languages, expert knowledge systems, and language-translation capabilities. Super-high-speed processing circuits are to be incorporated into its design, and its main memory will be extremely spacious by today's standards.

Parallel processing is another important goal, with perhaps as many as 1,000 processors working side by side to obtain the powerful computational capabilities the Japanese deem necessary for the next century of computer usage. Most of today's computers employ no parallel processing at all. When parallel operations have been attempted in large-scale machines, researchers have found that it is extremely difficult to get the various processors to work together in proper synchronization. The Illiac IV, which was completed in 1973 in a cooperative effort between NASA and the University of Illinois, was rigged with 64 parallel processors. It worked as advertised, but it never quite reached its design goal of 200 million operations per second in sustained and realistic trials.

Even when they have worked properly, supercomputers with parallel processing have never brought in big profits for their makers. Dr. Bruce H. McCormick of the University of Illinois summarized the results of previous large-scale projects as follows: "No supercomputer project in the past—whether it be the Univac Larc or the IBM Stretch or the Illiac—came near its stated goal or achieved commercial success." Perhaps the Japanese will be tenacious enough to manage a more favorable outcome. If they do build their Fifth Generation Computer, and it does end up with even a few of the capabilities they now envision, it will be a truly formidable competitor in the field of artificial intelligence.

Such a machine could also help them leapfrog America's next generation of industrial robots. Soon the average robot working in their labor-short land may be considerably more sensitive to its surroundings and considerably more intelligent than the primitive machines they now employ. If a part fails to fit, the robot will make a decision as to how to proceed. If it encounters a defect, it will make a different decision. If the assembly line chugs to a halt, or an important piece of machinery malfunctions, it will decide whether to conserve electrical power by shutting itself down too. In short, if computer technology continues to improve, the robot of the future will likely be an unusually versatile, responsive, intelligent machine. Someday it may even be able to pass the Turing test for machine intelligence.

CHAPTER 6

THE FACTORY
OF THE FUTURE

In 1974, when Donald Stansbarger at Northrop Aircraft first proposed his idea for the factory of the future—making high-performance military airplanes with robots—his colleagues were polite, but skeptical. Yet today, less than a decade later, some of his flaky concepts are becoming very real. "We admitted people would laugh at us, and sure enough, they did," he confided recently at his 11,000-square-foot plant in Hawthorne, California. "But we took our blinders off and went to work."

For years Stansbarger had dreamed of building an airplane with 60 percent graphite components. Graphite is an extremely versatile material. In one form it is the soft carbon in lead pencils. Grind it up and it becomes powdered lubricant. Punish it with intense heat and pressure and it coalesces into industrial diamond. Blend it with an aluminum matrix and it is magically transformed into a clothlike material with incredible strength and resiliency. "It's half the weight and three times as strong and stiff as aluminum," Stansbarger observes enthusiastically.

Unfortunately, when he and his fellow engineers tried to work with graphite, they found that producing large slabs of it by hand was prohibitively expensive. Eventually, after a few false starts, they hit upon the notion of combining sophisticated robots with relatively simple technology already available from the garment industry. In a small Northrop factory with strict limits on temperature and humidity, computer-controlled robots operate two 48-foot-long Gerber cutters of the type normally employed in slicing through multiple layers of cloth. They are used to cut paper-thin sheets of graphite later bonded into flat slabs of structural material.

Don Stansbarger is especially proud of the way he and his team of specialists have adapted existing technologies to solve new problems. "It's the same thing used to cut materials for suits, pants, and dresses," he says quietly. As he responds to my interview questions, he leans against an old auto hoist he and his team use to raise some of the machines to the proper height. "We inspect each station with overhead video cameras and will actually laminate the graphite structures with robotics and inspect the final assemblies with automated techniques," he points out. The robots also operate two large ultrasonic test systems and three X-ray units to ensure the production of graphite composites of uniform quality.

Northrop's factory of the future is a quiet, comfortable place to work; the technicians wear white jackets and cloth hats. The F-18 fighter, which they are making in conjunction with McDonnell-Douglas, is 9 percent graphite. Stansbarger thinks it will be 25 percent by 1985; and still he dreams of the day when it will be 60 percent. His dreams also include an even more futuristic factory, one that will be fully automated, with no need, except in emergencies, for human intervention. "Looking to the future," he says, as a bright look of boyish wistfulness ripples across his face, "I would love to turn it on in . . . 1990, stand back, and let it do its thing."

In fact, automated assembly operations similar to the ones Don Stansbarger envisions are already at work at a few locations. The Seiko watch factory in Japan provides one informative example. It assembles 100,000 mechanical wristwatches every month with a minimum of human effort and attention. Watches in dozens of different styles are produced automatically by robots in 1,000-watch batches.

A simple, low-technology robot starts the process by picking up a tiny plastic pallet and placing it on the assembly line. On the outside, the bathtub-shaped pallets are all the same size and shape, but their inside contours are all different; each one fits snugly around the particular watch being made. A magnetic memory in the pallet tells the various robots huddled over the production line exactly what operations to perform to assemble that specific watch. Every step of the process, including the insertion of the delicate hairlike mainspring, is carried out by robots, with one exception: mainspring adjustments are still handled by human craftsmen. If a robot makes a mistake, or if the watch fails to pass any inspection, a message is automatically stored in the magnetic memory of its pallet explaining to the human workers what went wrong and how the necessary repairs are to be made.

Seiko's automated assembly line, which is more than three miles long, seems entirely modern by American standards, but actually it was constructed in the 1960s. Most of the assembly operations are handled by simple pick-and-place machines so stupid and unresponsive that robotics engineers in this country would not even classify them as robots. American experts may be largely unimpressed, but Swiss watchmakers have developed a healthy respect for the technology of the Japanese. When Japan first began building automated factories, Switzerland held a preeminent position in sales of medium-priced mechanical wristwatches; today its market share is barely 50 percent.

Other countries are belatedly beginning to follow the Japanese lead in setting up factories with fully automatic assembly lines. In Erie, Pennsylvania, for instance, General Electric is constructing one of the world's most advanced assembly operations complete with computers, robots, and other dazzling symbols of advanced technology. Today 68 skilled machinists labor 16 days to produce a motor frame for a large locomotive. General Electric's new factory will turn one out every 16 hours—with no human assemblers.

The Japanese are also beginning to export their futuristic factories to other areas of the world. In Florence, Kentucky, a small Cincinnati suburb, robotics experts from Japan's Yamazaki Machinery Works are putting the finishing touches on a new $15-million machine-tool-parts plant, one of America's first fully automated factories. When the plant is completed, only 6 human workers will be needed to tend its master computer, keep an eye on the robots, and sweep the floor.

The factories developed by the engineers at Seiko and Northrop are sleek, impressive examples of modern automation. However, the so-called "factory of the future" involves much wider-ranging applications of computers, robots, and other automatic machines. Computers schedule the factory operations, maintain supply pipelines, design the necessary components, and "pre-test" them even before they come off the assembly lines. In effect, the entire factory becomes one giant computer-controlled robot.

The key to improved productivity in such a factory is the beneficial marriage of *computer-aided design* (CAD) and *computer-aided manufacturing* (CAM). In computer-aided design, the engineers use television-type CRT (cathode-ray tube) displays to work in concert with the computer in originating and modifying the blueprints and production plans for any new components to be made. In computer-aided manufacturing, they use the computer to schedule and operate the robots and other manufacturing machines on the factory floor for maximum practical output. When the two techniques are used together—as they often are—the combination is called CAD/CAM.

In this chapter I will discuss the practical benefits to be derived from CAD/CAM and the related technologies that will be used in the factory of the future. We will also see how automated robot delivery carts are being used to transport components and subassemblies from location to location inside the factory.

Computer-aided design relies upon the skillful use of a CRT display hooked to a computer. The designer feeds descriptions of his design into the computer by means of a typewriter keyboard and/or a light pen—an electronic magic wand that paints line drawings and other pictures onto a special television screen. On command, the computer straightens any ragged lines and closes any inappropriate gaps in the geometrical patterns supplied by the designer. It also responds to his instructions to alter the drawing in certain specific ways, such as adding or deleting lines. At any point the designer can command the computer to determine the approximate real-world behavior of his creation. For example, he might ask it to simulate how the part he is designing will behave under stress, or to determine how heat will flow through it if it is subjected to friction or solar radiation. If the results are unacceptable, he can use the light pen to modify the design in a number of ways to improve the part's performance.

Recently, I got an opportunity to talk to Jack Boddy, a computer-aided-design expert who works on the layouts and operation of the reusable Space Shuttle at Rockwell International. As we started the interview, Boddy cranked up a whirling magnetic disk drive. Its memory contained a three-dimensional wire-frame drawing of the contours of the Space Shuttle. "It took six hours to feed in all the lines," he told me, "but now that the model is in the computer, I can call it up and modify it any time I wish."

As he touched the light pen to specific sectors of the screen, the drawing seemed to take on a life of its own; it was a little like making a science-fiction film in real time. With a series of simple commands, he rotated the three-dimensional picture, enlarged sections of it, inserted new structural elements, and deleted unwanted lines, effortlessly and instantaneously. Whenever he wanted to keep what was on the screen, he casually punched a small red button, and the computer immediately printed a Xerox copy.

"It's easy to program most of the things you are seeing," Boddy told me with typical British understatement; "the hard part is making it suppress hidden lines. If the company hired an artist to sketch the Shuttle from several different angles, he could tell at a glance which lines were on the back side, hidden from view by other parts of the vehicle. But the computer doesn't have any sense of the real world, so it has to test all the surfaces two at a time to determine which are the hidden lines."

The computer programs used in computer-aided design often contain tens of thousands of instructions, which cost something like $50 each to code and debug. Jack Boddy's Space Shuttle program, for instance, includes instructions for determining the lift, the drag, and the aerodynamic heating of the rocket as it flies along its reentry trajectory through the earth's atmosphere. If any of these values turn out to be unacceptable at any point along its simulated flight, the contours of the Shuttle or the shape of its reentry trajectory can be changed for another try. In one afternoon Boddy can sketch numerous combinations and check out their consequences inexpensively in the safety of his office. In short, he uses the computer to conduct a series of realistic "experiments" to see how the Shuttle will behave under a variety of circumstances, making small improvements here and there until he is satisfied with the results.

He can even determine what would happen if some of the laws of nature were suddenly violated. For instance, the computer can be instructed to reverse the pull of gravity so that the earth *repels* the

Space Shuttle instead of *attracting* it. In this case, the vehicle will "fall" *upward* instead of *downward*. No matter how much money Congress appropriates for space research, NASA could never duplicate that "experiment" using real hardware. Such an exercise may seem pointless to the uninitiated. However, because of its versatility, the program, given a different set of inputs, can be used to simulate the behavior of a Shuttle-like craft flying into the atmosphere of a distant world such as Saturn, Mars, or Ganymede, one of Jupiter's moons.

The images on the CRT display are painted by electrons sprayed as a thin beam onto the screen by an electron gun in the neck of the picture tube. In effect, a CRT display is an *electronic* robot, which does its work with a thin finger of electrons rather than mechanical or electromechanical linkages.

Two different methods for forming the pictures on the CRT screen are in common use: *cursive* scanning and *raster* scanning. In cursive scanning, the computer draws the image directly, one line at a time, in the same way a professional cartoonist would do it. The basic element in a picture drawn cursively is the line segment, which may be straight or curved. In raster scanning, the computer paints the image one thin horizontal stripe at a time with a pencil-beam of electrons that moves over the back surface of the screen from left to right, top to bottom in a pattern similar to that used in an ordinary television set. In standard American black-and-white telecasting, the picture consists of 525 scanning lines of constantly varying shades of gray. The picture is repainted 30 times every second. When a picture with these characteristics is viewed at close range, it tends to have low resolution and bothersome flicker. Consequently, in displays used for computer-aided design, the number of scanning lines is often doubled. The number of separate pictures painted per second may also be quite a bit higher. Usually the screen is oversized and tinted green, since green images are easier on the operator's eyes.

Computer-aided design is so effective because the computer communicates with the designer in pictures rather than cryptic strings of numbers. The human mind absorbs pictorial information with surprising speed and accuracy. As one scientist put it: "Computer graphics seems to tap the way the brain is designed to work." Electronic pictures also facilitate the simulated testing and evaluation of the components being designed. The test results are superimposed, often pictorially, directly on the television screen. If the model is being heated, for instance, portions of it will be tinted in various colors each representing a specific temperature range. This helps the designer visualize the physical processes taking place.

An early program illustrating the basic concept of using computer graphics for industrial design was explored in detail by Ivan E. Sutherland in his doctoral dissertation at Harvard University in connection with an effort called "Project Sketchpad." The Sketchpad program was quite advanced for its day. Among other things, it could "erase unwanted lines either permanently or temporarily, fit... together the various pieces into a logical whole, [and]... move lines previously

RASTER SCANNING:
ELECTRON BEAM SCANS
ACROSS THE SCREEN HORIZONTALLY

CURSIVE SCANNING:
ELECTRON BEAM DRAWS
THE LINES DIRECTLY

The image on the screen of a cathode-ray-tube display is painted by a beam of electrons deflected by electromagnets in the neck of the picture tube. Two basic methods of scanning are widely used. In raster scanning, the beam of electrons sweeps out a series of narrow horizontal stripes running from the top to the bottom of the screen. In cursive scanning, the electron beam traces the outlines of the picture directly, one curved line segment at a time, in the same way a professional artist would do it.

drawn." It would also "refuse to draw lines that were meaningless in the context of the program at hand." Later Sketchpad-like programs were even more efficient and convenient. Researchers at the Rand Corporation, for instance, have developed a routine that straightens uneven lines automatically and replaces any ragged hand-lettered character with a flawless printed one. Lines can be removed by means of hash marks made over them, and new letters can be inserted by use of the proofreader's caret mark. The computer moves the other letters over on the screen automatically to make room for the new insertion.

In 1970, Dr. Sutherland published an article in *Scientific American* in which he systematically explored the powers of computer-aided design. Here is a small part of what he had to say:

> I think of a computer display as a window on Alice's "Wonderland" in which a programmer can depict... objects that obey well-known natural laws....
>
> Through computer displays I have landed an airplane on the deck of a moving carrier, ... flown a rocket at nearly the speed of light, and watched a computer reveal its innermost workings.

The methods used in designing and building the hydraulics system for the DC-10 commercial aircraft provide us with an instructive example of the power and promise of modern CAD/CAM techniques. The DC-10 is a plumber's nightmare. It contains more than 3 miles of convoluted hydraulic tubing that snakes around inside the airframe carrying pressurized fluids to various locations in a triply redundant hydraulic system. Until recently, the fabrication of the tubing involved complicated and expensive hand operations. The technicians began by building a full-size mock-up of the DC-10's hydraulic system. The resulting tubes were then disassembled and stored in a special warehouse to serve as "templates" whenever the workers needed to make a copy of a particular tube. Today CAD/CAM techniques are used instead. Consequently, the master tubes do not exist, and tube bending is no longer a manpower-intensive operation. Detailed bending instructions for each tube in the aircraft are stored in the computer's memory. By punching a few buttons the technician can call up the instructions for making any tube. He then presses another button, and within a few minutes the finished section of tubing emerges from a nearby tube-bending machine.

In the opinion of Gene Bylinsky of *Fortune* magazine, the payoff from the new system has been truly remarkable: "It's a lot more than just saving on warehouse space, although that, in itself, is substantial. The biggest benefit is that the tubes designed and fabricated under computer control fit into the airplane better, with fewer adjustments." With the old system, 12 skilled craftsmen were needed to make the necessary tubes, and it often took 6 weeks or more to get a finished part after the engineering drawings were released. About 100 tubes per aircraft did not fit.

Today 3 employees handle the same job. One watches the machine. Two assemble the finished tubes. Time from request of a tube until it is available: 18 minutes. On the average, only 4 tubes per aircraft must be discarded or adjusted by hand to achieve a proper fit.

Like most of the successful uses of CAD/CAM, the DC-10's hydraulic tubing is essentially a two-dimensional product (although some bends give a few of the tubes three-dimensional characteristics). Another important application of CAD/CAM is in the design of silicon circuit chips and the masks (stencils) used in their production. Circuits designed and produced in this way are cheaper, more capable, and easier to test by means of computer-controlled equipment. The printed circuit boards that connect the chips together are also designed and manufactured with the use of CAD/CAM techniques.

Computer engineer Ronald A. Cenowa at the Fisher Body Division of General Motors in Warren, Michigan, is a strong booster of computer-aided design. He points out that "Everything a draftsman needs is in the computer." He also notes that "Everything a draftsman conventionally does using triangles, pencils, compasses, and so on is done mathematically within this system." Moreover, the computer does things the designer would be hard-pressed to do on his own by any practical method. For example, it includes equations and algorithms necessary to "test" the system before it is built to see if it will meet design specifications.

The engineers at Fisher Body are using CAD/CAM testing techniques to study the behavior of passenger cars as they are driven over computer-simulated rough terrain. The car body wobbles and undulates in a purposely exaggerated manner as it hits make-believe bumps on a make-believe road. Flaws in design often become apparent before prototypes are built for real-world testing. Similar simulation procedures are being used at the International Harvester facility in

Hinsdale, Illinois, where a make-believe combine slithering over computer-created ice and snow strains to extract its wheels from simulated mud. The results help the research staff uncover design modifications for improved bad-weather performance.

Some CAD/CAM programs have even fancier capabilities. A few of them draw the successive shapes of a metal slab step by step as the finished part is gradually machined from it. Others can produce motion pictures showing how the various parts will interact when they are assembled into a functioning whole. The "flying eye" concept developed by the Applicon Corporation even allows the designers to go "inside" the assembly for a visual study of its interacting parts. Once they are inside, they get a view that might be completely impossible in the real world. For instance, the "flying eye" is used by automotive engineers to "view" at close range the moving flame inside the combustion chamber of an auto engine—an experience that must be something like living inside a V-8 engine as the car whizzes down the Santa Monica Freeway. As they "ride" in the automobile, they can modify its engine design to improve its flame characteristics or to reduce smog production.

The common notion of the great American industrial machine is one in which floods of raw materials move through the gate at shipping-and-receiving, and finished products flow in endless streams into waiting train cars for shipment to anxious consumers. Actually, such impressive efficiencies are being achieved in a few continuous-process industries such as petroleum refining and papermaking. However, most consumer and industrial products are presently manufactured in small batches rather than in continuous processes. Consequently, in most cases, self-adjusting feedback control cannot be used effectively to ensure quality and high performance. Fortunately, robots and computers can substantially enhance the efficiency of batch-processing facilities.

Another common misperception is that most of the products being made in our country are manufactured in mass-production quantities by large, dedicated machines. Actually, about 75 percent of our goods, by value, are made in small batch-processing plants. These factories typically turn out, at most, only a few dozen or a few hundred units of each type; consequently, it is impossible to justify the cost of expensive mass-production equipment. The impression we have when we visit such a plant is one of sadly inappropriate waste and inefficiency. As Thomas G. Gunn put it in a recent issue of *Scientific American*:

> The complexity of a modern factory is daunting: in some plants thousands of parts must be kept in stock for hundreds of products. Indeed, the complexity of the operations has sometimes led to a situation resembling gridlock on the factory floor: it is not uncommon for a metal part to spend 96 percent of the time required for its manufacture waiting in line for processing.

Moreover, it has been estimated that at least 50 percent of all manufacturing instructions sent into the factory by the design and production engineers are modified—or ignored—by shop workers during production and assembly.

Managing a batch-processing factory is enormously difficult. On the average, parts are in work only about 5 to 25 percent of the time, and scheduling the various operations is terribly labor-intensive. Some 60 percent of the people who work in batch-processing plants are doing something other than producing useful products. Poor organization causes them to have to work very hard. Gene Bylinsky describes the chaos in such a factory:

> In every plant in the country you see foremen running with "hot sheets" in their hands—a list of parts that are needed immediately on the assembly line. Some plants have more expeditors than people making things.

Somehow, it would seem, there must be a better way. There is. It is a part of "computer-aided manufacturing," and it relies heavily upon computer control of the production machines—both fixed automation and industrial robots.

Of course, the idea of using computers to control the machines in a factory is not new. In the 1950s, the U.S. Air Force set up a joint cooperative venture between the military and 20 major American companies. At first this "programmed machine-tool" effort was concerned mainly with the use of punched paper tapes to guide the operations of certain kinds of metal-working machines, but later versions were to use the precursors of modern industrial robots.

In 1959, while I was still in college, I flew to Oak Ridge, Tennessee, for a job interview with Union Carbide. While I was there, I learned at first hand about programmed machine tools. Union Carbide, along with 19 other large companies, was studying the feasibility of using punched paper tapes to control the operation of machine tools in the nuclear industry. At the time, I was convinced that this was probably one of the earliest applications of perforated tapes for control of production machinery. As a matter of fact, it was; however, the concept of using punched holes to control a manufacturing process is surprisingly old.

In 1801, Frenchman Joseph Jacquard employed wooden cards punched with patterns of holes to control his weaving looms. He used these cards to make colorful tapestries of incredibly intricate design. A hole in a card at a particular location caused the appropriate silk thread to end up on the face, rather than the back, of the cloth. Jacquard's tapestries were respected and admired throughout the civilized world, and for many years he was the toast of Europe. Dignitaries came from far and wide to see samples of his beautiful work.

Most of his tapestries were colorful forest scenes; but he also made a stunning self-portrait using 24,000 punched cards. His clever concept provided part of the inspiration to Englishman Charles Babbage, who later attempted to build the Analytical Engine. In describing the operation of the Babbage machine, his colleague Lady Lovelace wrote that it "weaves algebraic patterns in the same way a Jacquard loom weaves flowers and leaves."

The purpose of the marriage between CAD and CAM is to link the computers used by the designers with the computers used on the factory floor. However, in its ultimate form the factory of the future will have much more elaborate characteristics. Ultimately, computers will control the flow of parts and materials to the factory and the movement of products through the various stages of manufacture. At some facilities, the computers will be arranged in a hierarchy. A large-scale master computer will control smaller minicomputers responsible for operating sections of the factory. These computers, in turn, will communicate with smaller microcomputers each responsible for the operation of a single machine such as a robot or a programmed machine tool.

This arrangement is similar to the way the manpower in a large company is managed today, with separate groups, departments, and divisions arranged in a pyramid, responsible for increasingly larger operations. Just as the company president is unable to concern himself with all the day-to-day details of his far-flung empire, the master computer in the factory of the future will be forced to delegate some responsibilities to its electronic underlings.

If, for instance, the factory is assigned to manufacture a new lightweight bicycle wheel, the master computer might command three separate minicomputers in the middle of the hierarchy to fashion the rim, the spokes, and the hub. Of course, each component will require machining operations from various devices in the work cell being directed by the minicomputer. These separate machines (both robots and more conventional programmed machine tools) will be controlled in turn by microprocessor chips which execute the more general commands coming from the minicomputers at the next level of the hierarchy.

So far in this chapter we have considered the methods by which components will be designed and produced in a computer-directed manufacturing facility. But we have not looked at the ways in which parts and raw materials will be moved through the facility to the point of need. Conveyor belts, of course, will be used to bring many necessary items to the robots and other automatic machines. But another popular approach uses battery-powered robot carts that propel themselves through the factory, usually at a speed of a few miles per hour. A typical robot cart weighs about 700 pounds and can carry a payload as heavy as 500 pounds. Its batteries provide ample power for 8 hours of operation. They can be recharged with ordinary household current.

When the robot cart stops at prearranged points along its route, human workers and/or robots load and unload it. The route the robot is to follow is marked with copper guideways buried under the floor, or a trail of phosphorescent dye. The dye is invisible to the human eye, but it glows when exposed to an ultraviolet light on the bottom of the cart. It can be safely applied to carpeting, wood, concrete, or almost any other flooring material.

When the robot cart moves, it lets pedestrians know it is coming by beeping a horn and shining a light. In addition, it is rigged to halt automatically if it hits any barrier—person or inanimate object. Recently, I got an opportunity to watch the antics of a mail-delivery robot similar in function to the one just described. It was operating at the Naval Ocean Systems Center at Point Loma in San Diego, California. "At first people were scared of it," one of the sailors confided in me. "But the word soon spread that if it bumped into us, it would stop." He seemed enormously pleased that he would not be

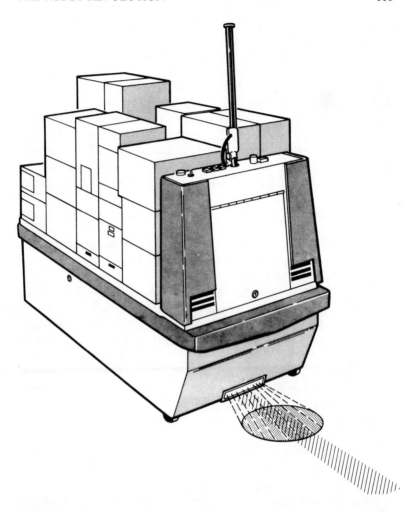

This Mailmobile, a driverless, battery-powered delivery robot, is manufactured
by Bell & Howell for use in the automated interoffice delivery of mail and other
small parcels. The Mailmobile follows a copper guideway under the carpeting
or a chemical trail painted on the floor. Normally the chemical is invisible,
but when it is illuminated by a special ultraviolet light on the bottom of the
cart, it glows. As the cart waddles along at a speed of about 1 mile per hour,
it beeps its horn and flashes a blue headlight to warn pedestrians. If it accidentally bangs into a person or any other barrier, special bumpers cause it to
stop.

bashed by a small robot tooling along at the pace of a lover's stroll.

Most robot carts are relatively unintelligent, but Bell & Howell is working on one that can be directed to choose between alternative paths and board an elevator. It signals the elevator, then waits with supreme patience for it to arrive before boarding. A smarter model now in the works will seek out the shortest route to its destination and share crossing paths with other, similar carts. Its program will include a special "safety" blocking feature to prevent collisions at the intersections.

Robot carts promise to help eliminate an enormous industrial bottleneck: the physical routing of small parts, paper, and documents. When the concept was first devised, some managers expected negative reactions from workers. Fortunately, most people in shops and offices seem to enjoy the new machines. David Larkin, Deputy Director of the Office of Administrative Services and Procurement at the U.S. Department of Commerce, is amazed at how delighted his workers are with their mailmobiles. "As for acceptance by the users, it is almost funny. We find that people will help the thing," he says. "You see them moving things out of the way." Often the robots are given endearing nicknames as a means of welcoming them to their new assignments. Common monikers include "Norman the Mailer," "Little Bo-Peep," "Bionic Box," "Cary R. Pidgeon," "Happy Honker," "Archie Bumper," and "Harvey Wallbanger."

The marriage of CAD/CAM with robots and other automatic machines is doing for small batch-processing industries what feedback control has always done for "continuous mode" industries such as papermaking and petroleum refining: it is giving them flexibility and high productivity with minimal human labor and supervision. Small wonder factory managers are poised to leap onto the bandwagon. Projections published by *Fortune* magazine indicate that over the next few years, companies that manufacture and market CAD/CAM systems will grow even faster than robot makers. Of course, the two enterprises will expand in tandem. Domestic CAD/CAM sales reached three quarters of a billion dollars in 1981, and if *Fortune*'s projections hold true, they should top $2.2 billion by 1984.

In a bold attempt to become the world supermarket of industrial automation in the 1980s, General Electric has earmarked half a billion dollars in investment capital. Senior Vice President Donald K. Grierson is clearly enthusiastic about the future potential of CAD/CAM. He maintains that it will "blast productivity through the roof." Many of his colleagues at General Electric and elsewhere share his optimism, believing that the broad-based use of computer-controlled machines in routine factory operations is an idea whose time has come. Indeed, conventional wisdom in the industry now holds that "CAD/CAM has more potential to improve productivity than any other development since electricity."

CHAPTER 7

ROBOTS AND MILITARY POWER

On May 14, 1982, the British destroyer *Sheffield* was on radar picket duty in choppy waters north of the Falkland Islands. It had been ordered there by Prime Minister Margaret Thatcher as part of an armada assigned to reestablish British sovereignty over disputed territory also claimed by Argentina. Unfortunately, after a brief skirmish with an Exocet missile skimming over the tops of the waves, the *Sheffield* lay crippled in the water.

The engagement began when an Étendard fighter-bomber launched the French-built Exocet missile toward the British destroyer 20 miles away. The pilot never saw his target, but less than 3 minutes after his forefinger punched the "launch" button, his sea-skimming missile struck the *Sheffield* amidships 6 feet above the waterline. Almost immediately, acrid smoke spiraled skyward over the deck of the destroyer. The fire quickly disabled many of the ship's operating systems, including most of its fire-fighting apparatus. "We tried to fight the fire for five hours, but I knew we were on a losing wicket," said Captain James Salt, the *Sheffield*'s commander. "On the upper deck you could

113

feel the heat through your feet with shoes on. The superstructure was steaming, and the paint on the sides was coming off... the hull was glowing red and hot... we had no hope of retaining the fighting capability of the ship." When the flames began spreading dangerously close to the destroyer's ammunition stores, Captain Salt gave the order to abandon ship. Later the burned-out hulk was scuttled. Twenty British sailors had lost their lives.

The Exocet missile, which stands 15.5 feet high and weighs 1,440 pounds, can be launched from an airplane flying as high as 6 and a quarter miles. Once it is released, it flies at about 500 miles an hour, swooping down to follow a flat trajectory 6 or 8 feet over the water. This hides it below the horizon out of sight of defensive radars, except for the last few seconds of the attack. Guidance from the point of release to the target is accomplished by an on-board computer that responds to corrective impulses from a radar altimeter, swiveling gyroscopes, and active homing radar. The radar normally takes over at a range of about 7 miles, guiding the missile relentlessly toward its target. Wind gusts, small performance anomalies, and changes in the target location all trigger corrective actions that tip and swivel the fins on the rear of the missile. As the missile approaches its destination, it rises slightly, scanning the horizon to make sure its terminal homing radar is locked on to the target. Its warhead, which weighs 350 pounds, is designed to first penetrate a ship's hull and then detonate.

The Exocet is a military robot. If you have trouble accepting that designation, compare it component by component with a modern industrial robot working on a Detroit assembly line. Both are rigged with computer "brains" and sensors to measure the world around them, and both have "muscles" to carry out their assignments. Most of the robots in Detroit employ actuators driven by hydraulic fluids or electric motors; the "muscles" of the Exocet are aerodynamic surfaces powered by hydraulics. Sophisticated assembly robots "see" the objects around them with television cameras and "feel" them with pressure transducers. The Exocet senses its environment with accelerometers attached to gyroscopically stabilized platforms and radar devices that help it maintain altitude and home in on its target— with deadly accuracy. As Lord Hill-Norton, retired admiral of the British fleet, put it when told of the sinking: "The *Sheffield* disaster proved that modern weapons do what most of us have said all along they would do: they hit instead of missing."

In this chapter I will discuss a variety of modern military robots,

The air-launched version of the Exocet AM 39 missile, which destroyed the British Sheffield off the coast of Argentina, can be launched from an airplane flying as high as 33,000 feet or as low as 300 feet. When the aircraft is within 40 miles of its target, the pilot releases the missile, then turns and heads for home. The Exocet dives down to the surface of the water skimming over the waves just below the speed of sound at an altitude as low as six feet. About seven miles from its target, the radar guidance system onboard the missile takes over to steer it onto a flawless collision course with its target. In the Falklands six Exocets were launched by Argentine military forces. Four of them struck enemy targets.

all of which are guided and controlled by computers so that they almost invariably "hit instead of missing." These will include missiles and rockets, remotely piloted vehicles, downsized ground-controlled experimental fighters, miniature robot tanks, and "doomsday machines" in the form of nuclear-tipped intercontinental ballistic robots.

H.M.S. *Sheffield* was a well-designed 4,000-ton destroyer protected by some of the most advanced defensive systems currently available. It had been built 10 years before at a cost of about $50 million. Yet it was sent to the bottom by a relatively small medium-range missile, a missile that has been described by its manufacturer as "an extremely reliable weapon capable of destroying any type of surface vessel with a kill probability of more than 90 percent." In the Falklands, under wartime conditions, six Exocets were fired by Argentina. Four damaged or destroyed enemy targets. All together, 114 aircraft and 10 ships were lost in the conflict by both sides. More than half were destroyed by "smart" robots.

The Argentine attack on the *Sheffield* was vaguely reminiscent of the kamikaze raids that devastated America's capital ships in the last few months of World War II. However, now that technology has given us robot brains and muscles to guide explosive projectiles toward their targets, much of the risk and glamour seems to be missing from modern war. No special bravery is required of a soldier who sits at a computer terminal watching flickering images on a television screen and pushing plastic buttons. As one battle-hardened reporter on the staff of *Time* magazine observed when he pondered the use of bloodless robots by the military: "It is no longer a matter of daring and courage. It has become a 20th century battle of the microchips and computers, of decisions far too fast for the human brain to make."

Military robots—on land, in the air, and at sea—fought on both sides in several important engagements in the Falklands. One of the most devastating incidents occurred with the sinking of the Argentine cruiser *General Belgrano*. As darkness descended, the aging 13,000-ton veteran of Pearl Harbor (then named the U.S.S. *Phoenix*) was steaming along at 10 knots toward the coast of Argentina. Crew members, many of whom would soon be dead, took catnaps, played chess, wrote letters, shopped in the commissary for candy and cigarettes. Suddenly, out of the silence, a British Tigerfish torpedo cut a zipperlike swath through the water. It had been fired by the *Conqueror*, a British nuclear-powered submarine. After launch, the Tigerfish plowed toward its target for 20 minutes at 60 miles an hour spooling out thin wires attached to the submarine's computer. Electrical impulses sent along the wires made constant corrections to the trajectory of the 3,400-pound Tigerfish. In effect, it was a robot on a 20-mile leash, guided along a varying path as directed by the computer.

A Tigerfish torpedo is whisper-quiet as it slips through the water. "It is one of the most deadly underwater weapons yet produced," claims one military authority. "It is virtually impossible for the target to know the torpedo is approaching." In fact, no one aboard the *Belgrano* did know anything unusual was happening until it was too late. "The torpedo exploded below the engine room, sending a shock and penetrating smell throughout the ship," explained Captain Hector Bonzo; "the ship was completely in the dark."

A second Tigerfish cut a gaping hole through the hull and sent a wave of burning oil across the deck, instantly cremating many sailors. Fire-fighting efforts were clearly hopeless, and Captain Bonzo sadly issued the order for his men to abandon ship. Those who made it bobbed up and down in the water aboard 50 orange life rafts waiting for their wounded craft to slip under. "At 17:00 the ship disappeared from the sea," the captain later reported. "The Argentine flag was not lowered from the *Belgrano*. It is waving four-thousand meters deep."

Now that computer-directed military robots are becoming widely available, *defensive* forces may be gaining the advantage in tactical war. Today, when offensive armies attempt to conquer new territory, they must expose their most valuable hardware to relatively cheap, but increasingly intelligent and effective, weapons of defense. In the Falklands, for instance, the $50-million *Sheffield* was sent to the bottom by a $200,000 Exocet missile. A similar event occurred in the 1967 Arab–Israeli war, when a small Egyptian patrol boat sank a $150-million Israeli destroyer with a single $20,000 Russian-built Styx missile fired from a range of 20 miles.

We have to go all the way back to World War I to find an earlier era in which the defender had such a clear-cut military advantage. In those days, defensive engagements were fought from protective trenches. Artillery fire from the big guns cratered the land between the two armies so badly it was almost impossible to move heavy equipment forward in parallel with the attackers. Running forward in the open without protection against enemy fire, the advancing foot soldier often had a battlefield life expectancy measured in minutes.

Some commanding generals reportedly referred to their troops as "cannon fodder"—a tasteless but gruesomely realistic characterization.

Aggressive war on a grand scale might have become impractical if technology had remained frozen or if brilliant new tactics based on mobility and firepower had not been devised. Unfortunately, World War II gave rise to the "Blitzkrieg" concept: swift surprise attacks involving precise coordination between ground artillery, close-support aircraft, and disciplined infantry troops. Blitzkrieg tactics, as pioneered by German military commanders, suddenly took the advantage away from the defender and as a result, Western Europe was soon engulfed in a smoke-powder nightmare. On both sides, raw "firepower" was seen as the key to victory. Tons of projectiles filled the air, often in the absence of a visible enemy. Estimates put together after the war by military researchers in England and the United States indicated that on average, it had required 300,000 rounds of small-caliber ammunition to kill a single enemy soldier.

The 1967 Arab–Israeli war is often cited as the turning point when raw firepower no longer prevailed. In that skirmish, new technologies—digital computers, modern methods of communication, and primitive military robots—apparently tipped the balance in favor of "intelligent" single-shot weapons, some having a double-digit probability—rather high by military standards—of destroying a valuable target.

Six years later, in the 1973 conflict between the same combatants, offensive Blitzkrieg tactics were strangely ineffective. For instance, when the 190th Israeli Brigade attacked the Egyptian Second Army in the Sinai under a solid umbrella of air support, it was virtually annihilated by wire-guided antitank weapons fired from lightly armored vehicles. After only a few hours of fighting, 130 Israeli tanks were reduced to rubble by Russian-made Sagger missiles each weighing barely 25 pounds. The effectiveness of these computer-directed weapons surprised nearly everyone, especially military planners in Israel. As Major General Chaim Herzog pointed out in his book *The War of Atonement: October 1973*, "The Israelis made a serious mistake in assuming that the best anti-tank weapon would be the tank." In fact, small, inexpensive military robots played a decisive role. This is how General Herzog described the litter left behind in one particularly devastating Sinai battle: "Hundreds of guiding wires lay strewn across the road as if a giant spider web had collapsed."

The kill rates achieved by some "smart" weapons are truly amazing. For instance, it is estimated that the Tow wire-guided antitank missile made in America has a kill probability of 80 percent up to its maximum range of 2.4 miles. Our Maverick air-to-surface antitank missile is even more deadly. In the late 1970s it made 208 direct hits in 226 test firings—a kill rate that exceeds 90 percent. Computer-directed weapons employ a variety of methods for locating and destroying their targets. Like space-age mechanical moths, some are attracted by the infrared rays emitted by hot surfaces (tank engines, aircraft exhaust gases). Others use optical or radar homing devices carried on board, and still others are directed by human "pilots" sitting on the ground viewing the battlefield on special television screens.

Cruise missiles now under development in the United States and the Soviet Union are considerably more capable than the primitive battlefield robots that were used with such deadly effect in the Mideast and the Falkland Islands. A cruise missile is a small, jet-powered, pilotless aircraft tipped with either a nuclear weapon or a conventional high-explosive warhead. One expert has described it as "a killer riding a computer."

The basic concept of the cruise missile is not new. The V-1 "buzz bombs" that terrorized London and other English cities during the Second World War were, in essence, cruise missiles. Although they got a great deal of press coverage, the V-1's were not very successful military weapons. Hundreds were shot down by antiaircraft fire. A few were dumped into the English Channel by brash British pilots. This they accomplished by flying in formation with the V-1 wing tip to wing tip, then nudging it to push it into a roll to induce a sharp dive. The V-1's were unguided; they were merely hurled in the general direction of their targets from parallel inclined launching rails. Highly compact microprocessor chips in today's cruise missiles will help them reach their targets along complicated, evasive trajectories even if enemy forces employ a variety of defensive measures. The cruise missile homes in on its target with electronic precision along a complicated low-altitude, terrain-hugging trajectory that shields it from enemy radar, antiaircraft fire, and surface-to-air missiles.

The Tomahawk cruise missile now under development in the United States provides an informative example of these advanced techniques. A special radar device pointed vertically downward constantly measures the missile's altitude above the local terrain. Unlike the V-2, which flew along a lofted parabolic trajectory over the English Channel, the Tomahawk screams along just under the speed of sound as low as 100 feet above the ground. If it is headed toward a hillside or other obstruction, it will automatically pull up to a safe altitude; once it gets on the other side of the hill, it quickly ducks back down again. On the way to its target, the missile follows a winding path to minimize its exposure to enemy radar installations and antiaircraft projectiles. Even in the vicinity of its target, it can make last-minute turns to confuse the enemy's defenses.

Guidance is accomplished by a clever marriage of optical sensors and digital computers. Most of the time, the cruise missile is guided along its trajectory by accelerometers mounted on swiveling platforms stabilized by gyroscopes. Unfortunately, the missile must fly for several hours in order to reach its target. During that time, navigational errors tend to accumulate, thus causing it to drift off course. Special trajectory corrections are achieved by "terrain matching"—a technique similar to the one you might use if you were hired to fly a small private plane from Dallas to Chicago. A digitized contour map of the territory the missile is to fly over is stored in the computer's memory. The computer automatically matches periodic radar "snapshots" of the ground below against the contours of its digitized map. This terrain-matching technique permits the Tomahawk to make regular and precise corrections to its trajectory, thus keeping itself on course.

According to its designers, the Tomahawk will be able to fly 1,500 miles along a preprogrammed trajectory with many turns along the way. As it flies, it will slip through protective valleys, at the end of its hazardous journey impacting within 300 feet of its target. Eventually, with emerging technology, the average impact error may be reduced to only 30 feet. This pinpoint accuracy will have important military benefits. For one thing, it will allow our forces to knock out hardened targets without leveling nearby cities and other civilian installations.

Five major types of cruise missile are now being developed by researchers in the United States. They will be launched from various platforms including airplanes, ships, submarines, and land-based launch pads located in NATO countries. Not surprisingly, the leaders in the Soviet Union are seriously concerned about the destabilizing effects of this new military capability. Consequently, their propagandists have waged an expensive campaign against the installation of cruise missiles on the European continent.

Although the Tomahawk is plagued by a number of developmental

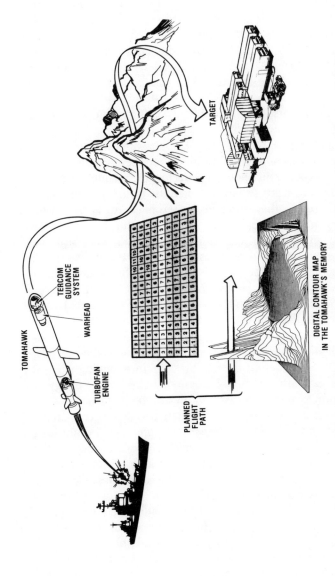

The land-attack version of America's Tomahawk cruise missile has a maximum range of about 1,500 miles. Once it is launched, it threads its way through valleys and over hills with clearances as close as 100 feet, hugging the ground to block the enemy's radar pulses and his missile defenses. As it flies, the Tomahawk's computer automatically surveys the landscape using its radar "eye" to make sure it is following the desired trajectory to its target.

problems including underpowered engines and a small possibility of enemy jamming, its project engineers are especially proud of the accuracy it has achieved under simulated battlefield conditions. In one recent test, it was launched from a submarine off the coast of California. It then flew inland 300 miles to a test range in the middle of a Nevada desert, where it split a cloth banner stretched between two poles.

For the past few years, hundreds of hardworking technicians at the Defense Mapping Agency in St. Louis have been preparing special digitized terrain maps for use by the Tomahawk cruise missile. A digitized map consists of a grid of numbers representing the average altitudes of blocks of terrain under the trajectory the missile is expected to follow in order to reach its target. When the technicians are mapping out the trajectory, they search for regions in enemy territory with sharp changes in altitude or other distinctive features the missile's radar can recognize. Surprisingly, snow cover and other seasonal changes cause only minor difficulties, but flat terrain can be much more bothersome. If the Tomahawk flies over a flat landscape, its radar readings may not be able to provide the computer with recognizable variations. Vast areas in the northern part of the Soviet Union are flat and featureless; but even so, the technicians at the Defense Mapping Agency are confident they can find enough distinctive landmarks to guide our robot bombs along paths leading to their targets. Their confidence stems from the fact that terrain matching is not a continuous process: it is used only occasionally, to update the gyroscopically stabilized navigation systems aboard the Tomahawk.

A modern cruise missile is a sharpshooter. It is designed to drop a single projectile onto a particular target with precision from a long distance. The U.S. Air Force is working on another weapon, the Wasp, which is more like a shotgun that fires a charge of intelligent buckshot. The objective of the Wasp program is to produce an effective "fire-and-forget" weapon that can be launched in groups against massed armored vehicles in a single pass over the battlefield. An airplane carrying the Wasp will be able to fire a salvo of up to 12 Wasp warheads. Visual contact between the pilot and the targets is not necessary; he merely flies in the general direction of the armored vehicles, then releases the appropriate number of warheads. Each individual warhead transmits radar pulses toward the ground and uses on-board data-processing techniques to analyze their echoes. This allows each warhead to recognize and attack its own specific target and to execute special terminal maneuvers to strike the most vulnerable area of that target.

Each General Dynamics F-111 and Fairchild A-10 will carry up to four Wasp pods, for a total of 48 missiles per aircraft. According to program officials at the Hughes Missile Systems Group, tests have demonstrated the ability of the Wasp to detect, identify, and track military targets even when they are hidden within strong ground clutter. If the Wasp goes into production, it will be very easy and convenient to use. The missiles, in batches of 12, will be inserted into their pods at the factory for shipment. No further assembly, maintenance, or checkout will then be required before they are launched in battle.

Robot aircraft can also be guided by teleoperators. During the 1982 Israeli invasion into Lebanon, the Israelis employed a number of remotely piloted vehicles (RPV's) operated by trained "pilots" sitting safely on the ground. Some of these RPV's were rigged to mimic the radar reflectivity of much larger military airplanes. When the Syrian defenders were tricked into turning on their radar transmitters to track the small unmanned decoys, the Israelis launched special "beam-riding" missiles to home in on their radar dishes, with punishing results.

In that same skirmish, the Israelis flew smaller RPV's over the battlefield to maintain reconnaissance. Two technicians operate a vehicle of this type. One "flies" it; the other, the "sensor operator," swivels the television camera, adjusts its zoom lens, snaps still pictures of interesting objects, and controls any other on-board sensors. When the conflict ended, mini-RPV's were used to monitor the pullout of the PLO. Manned surveillance aircraft could have been used instead, but they might have created serious political problems, complicating the withdrawal process.

Three years before the war, at the 1979 Paris Air Show, Israeli engineers had displayed a full-scale mock-up of their mini-RVP, which is called the Scout. The Scout is a pusher-type remotely piloted vehicle with a maximum gross weight of 260 pounds. Specification sheets handed out at the Air Show called for a top airspeed of 90 miles per hour, with a maximum endurance interval over the surveillance area of about 7 hours. The Scout is designed to carry a 50-pound payload of electronics and camera equipment. The principal element in its observation package is a television camera with a zoom ratio of 15:1. The camera, which is controlled by a remote "operator" by means of a secure radio link, creates a black-and-white picture with 625 scanning lines transmitted at 50 frames per second. Although it is classified as a medium-resolution picture by the standards of reconnaissance, it is considerably clearer and more stable than the image on your home television screen.

As it flies, the Scout is tracked through its data link. This position information is displayed in the corner of the television screen and recorded on the video tape. The tilt and swivel of the camera are also measured continuously, to allow the ground-station computer to determine and display the position coordinates of any object on which the camera cross hairs are centered. The date and the time of day to the nearest second are also displayed on each frame. If the camera operator notices an interesting target on the screen, he punches a button to mark the frame so that it will be easy to locate on the videotape at a later time. When the Scout is used to direct artillery fire, the operator marks the impact point of each round on the television screen with a light pen. The computer then automatically calculates the miss distance of each shell so that the gunners can be instructed by radio to make the appropriate corrections.

The "pilot" of the 260-pound Scout sits at a console rimmed with instruments similar to the ones in the cockpit of a small commercial airliner. A horizontal gyro displays the angle of climb, and a heading indicator shows the direction of travel of the RPV. Additional instruments indicate the vehicle's airspeed, remaining fuel supply, and other measures of performance. The on-board computer can be programmed to fly the Scout over a prearranged route, which can be overruled by the operator at any time, if desired. If no instructions are received from the ground, an on-board autopilot can maintain a constant altitude and/or a constant airspeed.

Although many of the Scout's military applications are classified, the Israelis recently gave foreign reporters a peacetime demonstration of its capabilities. Videotapes released by their government showed that the sensor operator was easily able to track the movements of selected motor vehicles winding along the streets of Beirut. In one sequence, the operator managed to track a helicopter in flight.

The Scout, which is launched by catapult, is retrieved in a net for refueling and reuse. Like everything else about the vehicle, the landing procedures are cleverly conceived. During the final approach, the "pilot" flips a switch so that he can watch the Scout from the vantage point of a special camera mounted on the ground looking up at a shallow angle through the net. In order to land it safely, he merely flies the craft so that its nose remains on the cross hairs superimposed on the image provided by the ground-mounted camera.

The American Sky Eye, which is about twice as big as the Scout, has a number of other impressive features which allow it to make independent "decisions" similar to those made by some of today's intelligent industrial robots. For instance, if jamming or intervening obstacles interrupt the Sky Eye's contact with its home base, it automatically climbs to a higher altitude. If this fails to reestablish radio contact, it swings around and heads for home to shorten the distance its control signals must travel. Unlike the Scout, the Sky Eye lands horizontally on wheels on a runway. According to the engineers who designed it, this gives the Sky Eye a more flexible theater of operations in military conflict and helps minimize routine maintenance.

Because remotely piloted vehicles have been so successful on the battlefield, some rather novel configurations are now being evaluated by military establishments all over the world. Researchers in Canada, for example, are working on a small bottle-shaped helicopter RPV rigged with two counterrotating propellers. It is intended for use in both surveillance and target acquisition. The vehicle, which will be covered with radar-absorbent material, directs its exhaust gases upward to minimize its detectability by infrared sensors. It is being tested at Suffield, Alberta, by its Canadian design-and-analysis team.

Lockheed Aircraft and ILC-Dover of Frederica, Delaware, have formed a team to study another novel approach called Hi-Spot. It will consist of an unmanned, remotely piloted dirigible with a 5-billion-cubic-foot envelope inflated with helium. The gasbag, which is made from Kevlar and Tedlar, two space-age plastics, is 504 feet long and has a diameter of 152 feet at its fattest point. Hi-Spot is designed to cruise at an altitude of 60,000 to 80,000 feet. Station-keeping and propulsive maneuvers will be handled by an 89-foot propeller mounted on the rear of the dirigible, which is being designed to remain aloft for as long as 5 months before it must descend for fresh supplies of fuel and helium. Preliminary engineering calculations indicate that Hi-Spot will cost only about one-tenth as much as a geosynchronous satellite with equivalent reconnaissance capabilities.

Reconnaissance is not the only practical application for remotely piloted vehicles. The concept has also been used effectively in the testing of high-performance manned military aircraft. Rockwell International's HiMAT (Highly Maneuverable Aircraft Technology) program provides us with an instructive example of this imaginative approach. Usually, when aircraft engineers are assigned to design and build a new high-performance airplane, they start with a small, unpowered scale model which is tested for hundreds or thousands of hours in subsonic and supersonic wind tunnels. Later, one or two full-size versions of the aircraft are built and tested in a series of increasingly demanding flights under the cautious control of human test pilots. In the HiMAT program, however, the wind-tunnel tests were followed by the construction of two working models which were built one-third size and flown as remotely piloted vehicles by "pilots" located on the ground. The two vehicles were equipped with composite wings that could be removed and replaced to test various geometries and construction techniques.

The test flights of the HiMAT RPV's provided a number of important practical benefits over more conventional flight-test procedures. For one thing, the test vehicles were much smaller than full-size airplanes, and hence were considerably cheaper to build and operate. Moreover, they did not need to be fully man-rated for safety, because a failure would not likely result in loss of human life. Finally, the test program could be accelerated with much more aggressive and imaginative flights because the vehicles were expendable. The major test objectives were to fly the airplane through certain critical test points to demonstrate its inherent stability and control and its ability to operate for a sustained interval under 8 g's of acceleration. These objectives were met without mishap.

Of course, the concept of using RPV's to test the HiMAT also involved a few disadvantages. For one thing, it was surprisingly difficult to scale down some of the hydraulic and electronic components of the full-size HiMAT so that they would fit within the fuselage of the two smaller test vehicles. Ensuring crew safety for the servicing and launching of a non-man-rated aircraft was also considerably more difficult than mission planners had originally supposed. Still, when the test flights were all completed, NASA and the Air Force were pleased with the outcome. "The HiMAT approach is a practical way to test an airplane in a cost-effective and efficient manner," wrote one of the participants in a technical paper summarizing the lessons they had learned.

The results obtained by Scout, Sky Eye, and HiMAT suggest that it may be possible—and beneficial—to construct remotely piloted fighter and bomber aircraft to carry out military missions over enemy territory. Retired Admiral Noel Gaylor, former Commander in Chief of the U.S. Forces in the Pacific, has carefully reviewed the problems pilots encounter when they are assigned to attack military targets that are protected by "smart" projectiles. His studies have convinced him that manned attack fighter aircraft are just about obsolete. "The attrition to opposing missiles will make them impractical," he says forcefully. "I think we should go to robot fighting vehicles." Unmanned flying robots of the type he envisions could be built large or small, or any scale consistent with their missions. The absence of a pilot would also eliminate all human-oriented limits on temperatures, pressures, and g-loads, thus permitting extremely tight turns in aerial dogfights and dive-bombing runs. Moreover, RPV's could be ordered to fly extremely hazardous missions because they would be cheap and readily available and they could be regarded as expendable hardware even in minor conflicts. The attempt to rescue our hostages in Iran, for instance, might have been pushed to its conclusion, success or failure, if there had been few or no human military personnel aboard the rescue craft. Robot tanks aboard the rescue craft, controlled remotely and equipped with automatic weapons, could have been used to overpower the Iranian captors. As things stood, we were forced to withdraw in the middle of the mission, in part because the further risk to human beings was judged to be much too great.

From the foregoing descriptions, it seems clear that intelligent battlefield robots will be widely used in future military engagements. In addition, conventional industrial robots will continue to help in the production of our war-fighting hardware. As we saw at the beginning of Chapter 5, the industrial robots at Northrop are already at work making graphite composites for high-performance military airplanes such as the F-18. Robots also handle and machine artillery shells, and they are used in spot welding and component assembly in the making of conventional military vehicles, including tanks and jeeps. Intelligence reports indicate that Russian vehicles being used in Afghanistan are produced, in part, by robots imported into the Soviet Union from Japan.

Technicians at the Autonetics Marine Systems Division of Rockwell International in Anaheim, California, have trained an agile robot they call "Mr. Superclean" to eliminate tiny contaminating particles in their precision military gyroscopes. Mr. Superclean is ideally suited to this task, because his gripper is far cleaner than the hands of a human being. As a matter of fact, he is considerably cleaner than a brain surgeon who has just finished scrubbing his hands for the mandatory 4½ minutes prior to entering the operating room.

The gyroscopes being decontaminated by Mr. Superclean are key components in the navigation systems to be used in nuclear-powered submarines. Extreme accuracy is necessary, because a nuclear sub must be able to move about underwater for several months without navigational updates. The requirements for precision and cleanliness of these gyroscopes are almost beyond human comprehension. Proper operation depends upon the precise rotation of a small metal ball which must be machined into a spherical shape within $\frac{1}{50,000}$ of an inch—or about one sliver from a human hair split lengthwise into a thousand pieces. As it spins, the ball clears the sides of the cavity in which it is mounted by $\frac{1}{2,500}$ of an inch. Microscopic particles can spoil the performance of the gyroscope. H. W. "Bill" Hanebaum, division manager of Advanced Manufacturing Technology at Autonetics, gestures with wild animation as he describes why the gyroscopes his company manufactures must be so incredibly clean:

> The gyro is one of the most accurate instruments manufactured in the world today, with part tolerances in the two-to-four-millionth-of-an-inch range. The rotating element spins at three thousand four hundred revolutions per second. These factors, coupled with the ultrahigh lift-off voltages involved, demand a level of cleanliness an order of magnitude above that required by more conventional gyros.

In a chamber filled with pressurized nitrogen, Mr. Superclean carefully sprays the precision gyroscopes with filtered liquid Freon. The nitrogen gas keeps out contaminating particles and helps prevent moisture from forming. Human beings are able to work in a nitrogen chamber only if they wear oxygen masks—which themselves tend to add harmful contaminants. The robot's hand requires no protection when he cleans a gyro. Humans must wear surgical rubber gloves, which slough off contaminating particles regardless of their quality.

The technicians at Rockwell are impressed with the speed and agility of their robot. His arm moves both vertically and horizontally as he carries out his assignment. It also extends, rotates, and opens and closes its gripper. All of his motions are controlled to a precision of one-thousandth of an inch, an accuracy superior to what any human being can achieve under the same conditions. Mr. Superclean cleans a gyroscope in 14 minutes. A human technician must work for several tedious hours, even days, to complete the same assignment.

In future years, as military robots become cheaper and more capable, front-line military commanders will almost certainly use them in increasingly large numbers. In the distant future, there may be no human soldiers at all on the battlefield. Instead, train carloads of military robots may be shipped to the battleground to engage in modern mechanized jousting, to ascertain, by proxy, which of their sponsors should be declared the ultimate victor.

In 1981, a special steering group of experts was established by the U.S. Army to determine how robotics and artificial intelligence could enhance the performance of soldiers on the battlefield. Their report, which was published in September of 1982, recommended that military research efforts be concentrated on autonomous combat vehicles and autonomous subsystems, such as automatic shell loaders for tanks. Remote-controlled obstacle-breaching vehicles were also singled out for further study. Such a vehicle would be sent across a minefield to explode any buried mines on contact.

The Army's 9th Infantry Division has already conducted several tests with remote-controlled tanks at its White Sands Missile Range. In one demonstration, a computer directed the movements of ten experimental tanks from a distance of 60 miles. Potential combat applications are also emerging from planning sessions. As one military researcher gleefully observed: "The possibilities for decoy, deception, and harassment are numerous!"

In a related effort, the Army's Night Vision Laboratory is working on a small remote-controlled vehicle with a 15-foot mast-mounted sight. It would amble across the battlefield at night on patrol, using its special optics to spot troop movements or other suspicious activities without risk to human soldiers.

In 1983, Colonel Charles J. Garvey and Dr. James J. Richardson published a joint survey article in the defense journal *Military Electronics* dealing with unmanned robot tanks. One of the biggest advantages of their concept is that a robot tank can be much smaller than its manned counterpart. This makes it considerably harder to detect and destroy in combat. Military designers in the Soviet Union have long recognized this fact; consequently, their tanks are tons lighter and considerably smaller than ours, partly because their tank corps are limited to small men. In addition, the latest Soviet tanks employ automatic shell loaders, reducing their crew size to 3. As Garvey and Richardson observe: "The resulting impact...on logistical support, transportability, and survivability is obvious." Here is their description of the rationale U.S. military planners should follow in building miniature unmanned tanks:

> It has become axiomatic that tanks carry a crew of four. A gunner, a loader, driver, and commander are stuffed into quarters which make submarines appear spacious. Even so, the penalties in weight of housing four crewmen are significant since weight varies as the square of the enclosed volume.... Further the [tank's] silhouette is predictably large....
>
> Question: Why four men? Answer: There need not be. Add an automatic loader—exit one man. Improve the gunner's vision and ease of targeting—exit another man. Provide the tank with some steering intelligence and the driver with 360-degree optics and fire control—exit the third man. Give the tank computer and sensor capabilities to maintain a heading while avoiding impassable terrain and directing and delivering fire—exit the last man.

Garvey and Richardson are convinced that their approach will produce huge manpower savings while providing us with an effective armaments platform which is much more survivable and expendable than the manned tanks now making up the backbone of our land attack forces. "Rather than a huge 60-ton steel vehicle carrying four men, we envision perhaps a roboticized six-foot-high light vehicle with one man, or a crewless four-or-five-foot-high, two-ton vehicle where only electronics will be endangered."

The "brains" of a robot tank could be located in the tank itself; but it may be more practical to control it via radio and television links from a nearby command post—or from a larger manned tank assigned to supervise the overall operation of a squadron of smaller robot tanks on the battlefield. In any case, limitations on available radio frequencies will dictate that the tank itself have at least enough on-board intelligence to avoid routine obstacles such as gullies and trees. It will also monitor its own health status and maintain at least minimal damage control—dousing internal fires automatically and switching to redundant subsystems if it suffers hits from shell fragments or battlefield lasers.

The obvious advantages of robot tanks include (1) their ability to operate in hazardous situations without emotion, (2) the lack of human needs such as food and sleep, (3) the ability to operate reliably for extended intervals, and (4) a reduction in the politically sensitive prisoner-of-war problem.

Promising battlefield applications spring to mind immediately. In particular, robot tanks could serve in the dangerous role of "point man" in a major infantry attack. They could also be used to clear minefields, to perform dangerous reconnaissance missions, and to aid in the construction of bridges and airfields under sustained enemy fire.

Simpler resupply vehicles would also be useful. They could follow preprogrammed routes carrying fresh supplies such as food, ammunition, and new robot tanks to the battlefield. Similarly, low, flat robot stretchers could retrieve the wounded. And their mechanized cousins could act as "sniffers" detecting nuclear, biological, or chemical materials dispersed by the enemy. Garvey and Richardson view applications of this type as a great step forward in more humanitarian military operations. As they put it: "If we were to go to war today, soldiers would be ordered to cross a river on a patrol mission to check out a contaminated area. Given modern [robotics] technology, such missions are Neanderthal."

Dr. Edward Teller, father of the hydrogen bomb, has long maintained that hot, heavy, hazardous, and monotonous tasks in war are ideal assignments for robots. Moreover, he believes that given proper hardware and software, there is essentially no limit to what we can expect from tomorrow's highly trained battlefield robots. "Unmanned vehicles can be used for reconnaissance, for attack, or for defense—for anything you please," he writes. "What a man can do, an unmanned vehicle can do."

Dr. J. Bart Czirr and Dr. E. Paul Palmer, both of whom teach in the Physics and Astronomy Department at Brigham Young University, have been toying with a concept that is even more bizarre than robot tanks. They propose a method whereby robots could become the ultimate deterrent against nuclear war by ensuring the destruction of the Soviet Union after a first strike—even if the Soviets should manage to kill every single person in the United States! Naturally, if the Soviets understand that a sufficiently devastating retaliation inevitably awaits them, they would never dare strike first. Czirr and Palmer call their novel concept the "boomerang" system. It would rely upon small, unmanned submarines which would remain submerged for months on end. Each robot submarine would carry several nuclear-tipped missiles capable of flying across intercontinental distances. The missiles would be aimed toward all the major population centers in the Soviet Union, and they would be programmed for automatic launch at predetermined times. There would be only one way the launches could be stopped: if the submarine received an encrypted "All is well" message from military commanders in our country. The absence of such a message at any time—presumably in the aftermath of a nuclear attack on the United States when no authorized personnel are left to send it—would automatically trigger the launch of the missiles.

Such an approach would be a chillingly effective deterrent. As Czirr and Palmer put it: "The system would fulfill its mission automatically, weeks, months, or years after the attack, even after the country was utterly destroyed." Robots would wield total power over our destiny; but no sane Soviet commander would seriously consider initiating a nuclear strike against our homeland. Such an undertaking on his part would be entirely pointless. The only possible outcome would be total, inevitable annihilation of his entire country by our unconcerned robot "doomsday" machine.

CHAPTER 8

SHOW ROBOTS

They came from small-town America in mud-streaked Chevrolets and rumbling Model-T Fords bound for the World's Fair in a meadow outside New York City. They came to see John Deere tractors and home-baked rhubarb pies, Hereford cattle and steel-framed Ferris wheels. Hope for the future was in short supply in that final, grinding year of the Great Depression. But on that day, before they headed back home, a few of them found fresh hope when they got an opportunity to witness a riveting vision of the future.

Even in 1939, during the final year of the Great Depression, it was great to be a tousle-haired 12-year-old in America. All day he had felt strangely elated wandering among the many exhibits; but now his father and mother were nowhere to be seen. A lump formed deep in his throat; his eyes searched the faces in all directions. Suddenly, he spotted a gigantic metal man shuffling through the crowd. "Jeepers! I thought those guys were only in the movies. He's talking —to me!"

"Hello there, young man. My name is Electro. I have come here to tell you all about the latest labor-saving appliances from the people who made me at Westinghouse."

A familiar hand warmed the boy's shoulder.

"Hey, Dad! Look at the giant robot man. Do you think we could get one like him? We could feed him peanuts . . . and gasoline, and he can sleep in the garage—or at the foot of my bed."

A pair of anxious eyes scanned the father's weather-beaten face.

"Well, now, I don't know if we can get a robot of our own," he said finally; "but he sure is impressive, isn't he?"

Later, an engineer explained to the crowd how Electro had come into being at Westinghouse in a project begun a decade earlier, near the end of the Roaring Twenties, when "mechano-anthropologist" Joseph Barnett developed "Televox," the first in a series of walking, talking mechanical men. Televox was followed in 1932 by "Willie Vocalite," a mechanical creature who could sit up, fire a gun, salute, and speak in a deep baritone. Vocal coaches were called in a year later to teach Willie to sing some of the catchy show tunes of the day. In 1939 he went back into the shop for a complete overhaul. While on the bench, he was outfitted with a sparkling new metal skin, his "nervous" system was rewired, and his vocabulary was improved.

In that same year, Electro—the ultimate of the early Westinghouse robots—was born as a full-grown metal giant. His movements were more versatile and precise than those of Willie Vocalite, and he towered over the spectators at a height of 7 feet. His chest expansion was 82 inches. Of course, his chest was always expanded; it was a rigid aluminum shell stretched over a steel framework. Electro loved to dance and play, but he had trouble buying sneakers. His feet were 18 inches long and 9 inches wide, and thick cables passed through holes in his heels to carry electrical power into his body.

"Electro is as smart as the average ten-year-old," the engineer told the crowd, "but he has a vocabulary of only seventy-seven simple words. He never gets hungry, and he speaks only when spoken to." Electro's "brain," which weighed 60 pounds, was crammed with 82 electromechanical relays, 2 electric eyes, and a number of signal lights to control his 26 different movements. The relays operated motors, gears, and chains to permit the large, lumbering mechanism to walk, talk, count numbers, distinguish colors, and give a smart military salute. Like many of his contemporaries, Electro enjoyed chasing

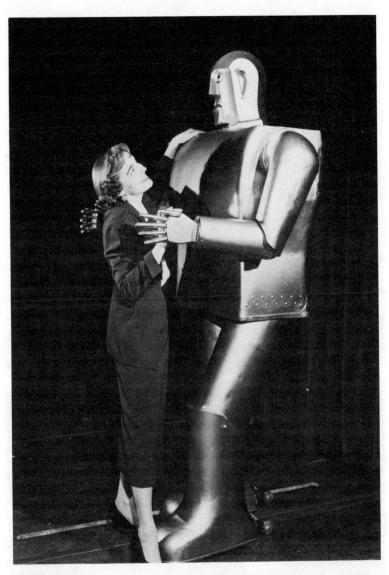

Electro, the biggest, the best, and the last of the promotional robots built at Westinghouse, was born full-grown in 1939. When he was not busy smoking cigarettes and flirting with the sassy young ladies in the audience, he and his robot dog Sparko were usually introducing fancy new electrical appliances to the American public. Notice the power cables running into the heels of his huge feet. Electro and Sparko were permanently retired shortly after World War II. They have since been dismantled.

women and smoking cigarettes; Chesterfields and Camels were his favorite brands.

One-syllable words spoken into a small microphone tucked in his ear activated and controlled Electro's behavior. A two-word command started a movement; a one-word command stopped it. All spoken commands were converted into electrical impulses; consequently, any word or words at all would do. Of course, the technicians tried to choose commands that made Electro's behavior appear responsive and intelligent. Red and green filters placed over his "electric eyes" (photoelectric cells) gave the robot primitive color-recognition capability—a trick that invariably pleased and amazed his enthusiastic fans. An observer stationed nearby carefully monitored Electro's programmed motions. If necessary, he could flip a switch to cancel any hazardous or inappropriate command.

In 1940, two mechanical dogs, "Sparko I" and "Sparko II," were constructed to accompany Electro and Willie Vocalite on their sep-

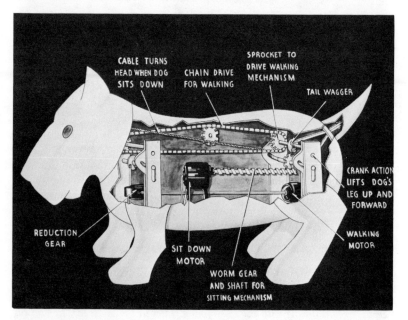

The public never realized it but "Sparko" the robot was actually identical twin canines. This early cutaway drawing reveals some of the clever drive mechanisms that allowed Sparko to walk, sit, beg, and bark and to engage in other realistic doglike movements.

arate publicity tours. Among other things, the Sparko twins could walk, bark, beg, and wag their tails. After the United States entered the war, the Sparko dogs, Willie Vocalite, and Electro were all placed in temporary retirement, but when hostilities ended in 1945, they were called back to work. For a few years thereafter, they did a commendable job of demonstrating the many new consumer products made at Westinghouse.

In this chapter we will see how robotic devices are used for promotional purposes and entertainment. Show robots similar to, but much more advanced than, Electro and Willie Vocalite will be included, together with movie-star robots. Those versions which are used to entertain guests at amusement parks and pizza parlors will also be described. We start with movie robots that have often graced the silver screen—some real, others fake.

Over the years, a few daring moviemakers have attempted to use robots that are actually operated by remote control. *Buck Rogers in the 25th Century* and *Silent Running*, for instance, contain noteworthy examples of robotic devices of this type. Unfortunately, in most cases these genuine film robots have been miserable failures because they lacked sufficient dexterity to execute convincing lifelike motions. Their clumsy articulations not only failed to please the critics; they also perpetuated the image of robots as stupid, unthinking machines. Then as now, the more successful science-fiction films almost invariably featured "robots" that were professional actors dressed in clumsy robot suits.

Until recently, digital computers were as big as refrigerators and weighed several hundred pounds, so they could not be carried comfortably aboard a robot. Consequently, if control was accomplished by computer at all, it had to be handled by a back-room computer linked to the robot by radio. However, even the biggest available computers did not have enough computational power to give a movie or promotional robot smoothly articulated movements resembling those of its human counterpart. For this reason, most of the people building show robots soon concluded that for their purposes, the human brain was superior for real-time decisions, and the human fingers offered the best method of control. A radio transmitter sent signals to the robot from a special hand-held control unit. In short, promotional robots came to resemble movie "robots" in function and appearance, whereas their control systems were patterned after those used by industrial teleoperators.

One of the first successful show robots of this type was constructed by Tony Reichett of Quasar Industries. His brainchild was rigged with a cone-shaped body 5 feet tall capped with a luminous bulb head. It weighed 250 pounds. Taking the name of the movie robot that shared top billing in the film *The Day the Earth Stood Still*, Tony called his creation the "Klatu" Sales Promotional Robot. Often in the early 1970s, Tony Reichett could be spotted wandering arm in arm with one of Klatu's identical brothers, weaving among the startled patrons at a local shopping center or an industrial sales convention. The shock of seeing a mechanical creature ambling along in public was much greater in those days because neither industrial nor promotional robots had received much publicity in the popular press.

Even when they managed the difficult task of constructing a workable robot, most hobbyists had no clear idea how to get enough media attention to attract a profitable clientele. Fortunately, a publicity-conscious entrepreneur from Irwindale, California, quickly mastered that part of the business. His name was Gene Beley. Beley found his avocation by a circuitous route. First he formed a small company called "Games People Play" which specialized in supplying action-packed pinball machines and video games to amusement arcades. In the mid-1970s he changed the name of his company to "Android Amusement," at the same time becoming the West Coast representative of Quasar Industries. From that day forward, Beley and his clever creations have managed to dominate the show-robot business.

Gene has always liked the name "Android Amusement" because he feels that it accurately reflects his own individual approach to the business. Unlike many of his colleagues, he operates from the premise that show robots are nothing more than a clever form of amusement. A few small robot makers have shunned promotional applications, instead attempting to market household robots as servants. This may seem like a reasonable approach, but so far, all the companies that have tried it have failed financially. Their biggest problem centers around the fact that it is so difficult to build a household robot that can perform useful and impressive tasks.

A few years ago, Gene Beley severed his relationship with Quasar Industries and co-developed his own family of show robots in conjunction with a new partner, Ray Raymond. They designated their new mechanical family the "Argon" series. More recently, Gene has concentrated on his much more successful DC ("Drink Caddy") robots. A number of celebrities, including *Playboy*'s Hugh Hefner, have

This Drink Caddy 2 promotional robot built by the Android Amusement Corporation of Irwindale, California, includes a computer keyboard for control and a chest-mounted television monitor capable of displaying promotional messages. The DC-2 is representative of a new breed of robots expressly designed for the rugged show environment. Custom-molded fiber glass and polished metal components add a touch of elegance.

purchased Drink Caddy robots from Gene as novel, but expensive, gadgets for entertaining party guests. In addition to carrying a serving tray loaded with mixed drinks, the Drink Caddy livens up a party's atmosphere by playing prerecorded music.

DC also has a television set built into his chest which displays commercial messages and allows him to challenge party guests to play video games. Gene Beley is not sure he understands why, but he has noticed that people totally anthropomorphize promotional robots. His creations have been punched by frightened kids and kissed by curvaceous brunettes. One was shoved down a stairwell by a belligerent old lady.

One of Gene Beley's DC-2 creations has a police record. The incident began in September of 1982 when, according to the *Los Angeles Times*, a robot was "arrested" by two police officers in Beverly Hills for illegally handing out business cards on a busy street corner. When the police were unable to locate its owner, they decided to haul the ornery critter to the station house for solicitation of business on a public sidewalk. However, when the officers tried to disconnect the robot's battery pack, it fled from them, screaming in a panicky voice, "Help me! They're trying to take me apart!" DC-2 was later retrieved by Dave and his two sons (who were responsible for the incident) at the Beverly Hills police station. Dave had to pay a $40 towing charge.

Of course, things even out. Three months later, in December of 1982, a robot working on the other side of the law helped police foil a major crime. The incident occurred in Deerfield Beach, Florida, after the police department got a phone call from an extortionist who claimed that he had placed a package of explosives in a supermarket. He indicated that he would detonate it by remote control unless he was paid "a large sum of money." The police responded by sending a robot into the store. Once inside, it placed the packaged explosives in a shopping cart and pushed them out to the parking lot. Then, as a crowd of fascinated shoppers looked on, the robot carefully opened the package and defused the bomb.

David Coleman, a competitor of Gene Beley's, has developed a curiously different approach to the promotional-robot business. Dave started his career as a professional skater with the Ice Capades and the Ice Follies. More recently, he formed a business in Cascade, Colorado, called "The Robot Factory." His first creation, "Commander Robot I," was an ice-skating demon made of aluminum and Plexiglas. Commander's main mission in life was to skate swiftly across the ice while performing acrobatic stunts to keep the fans, young and old alike, laughing and enjoying the show. Two motors drive Commander, whose operator can steer him along a wavy trajectory by speeding up one motor or slowing down the other. If one of the motors is running in forward, the other in reverse, the robot spins in tight circles.

Dave's later creations include a whole family of ice-skating robots: creeping worms, pesky bugs, and warm "fuzzies" each with its own playful personality. One of them, whose name is "Bagley T. Brat," is a furry, Muppet-like creature who rides a tricycle across the ice; Dave chose the name because his creation "looked like a brat riding on a motorcycle" when he saw him tearing along across the rink. Commander I is 8 feet tall, but Dave's "worms" skitter across the ice at a height of only 3 or 4 inches. They are made of green urethane foam, and their menacingly cute faces are dominated by pleasing smiles. Dave and his creations have appeared at national conventions and on network television. One of his favorites was stolen, but the thief soon brought it back. Evidently, he could not figure out how the rebellious critter was supposed to work.

When Dave Coleman left the Ice Follies in 1978, he and his creations received an invitation to appear on the *Merv Griffin* television show. Unfortunately, the robots were designed for vigorous movements across the ice, not for walking on dry land. Dave accepted Merv Griffin's invitation, but he and his crew had to spend three months modifying the robots so they could "walk" into the studio to greet their appreciative host.

The wild antics of promotional robots may impress and amuse the members of professional robotics societies; but many experts resist the notion of calling such primitive, imprecise devices robots at all. As one society member put it: "They should never be overglorified with the name 'robot.' They may be fun to watch, but they are nothing more than sophisticated, remote-controlled toys, with little or no useful function." Fortunately, some industry professionals are blessed with a much more tolerant attitude. A few of them attempt to follow the best experimental work of today's promotional-robot builders. Over the years, they have come to appreciate the outstanding research contributions by a few of the best amateurs in such important frontier technologies as speech recognition and speech synthesis. Automatic computer control and manipulator technology are also being advanced by some dedicated hobbyists.

Joseph Engleberger, president of Unimation, combines the expertise of a cool professional with the enthusiasm of a playful hobbyist. Most of his attention is devoted to building large, ugly industrial robots that are bolted to the factory floor and perform the same routine tasks over and over again; but he has also instructed the engineers on his staff to build a mobile service robot named "Isaac" (after science-fiction writer Isaac Asimov). No doubt Joseph Engleberger is hoping to get a little free media attention; but he also foresees useful tasks for Isaac. Eventually, Engleberger is convinced that his robot will be able to "serve coffee to visitors, clean up afterward, and be capable of performing such household chores as washing windows and watering plants." He also believes that "the descendants of Isaac will be able to maintain home appliances, fight fires, even play Ping-Pong."

Thomas Carroll of Long Beach, California, is another robotics experimenter who is attempting to bridge the gap between the simple technology used by the hobbyist and the more sophisticated approach usually adopted by the professional. For nearly 20 years Tom has been a professional aerospace engineer; consequently, when he set up a small robotics consulting firm in 1978, he was already familiar with the latest innovations in electronics and manipulator technology. Although he has built a number of interesting robots over the years, his chief interest lies in helping others develop their own state-of-the-art promotional robots. The two most successful projects of his company, Universal Robot Systems, have been the "Squirt" and the "Colossus" series robots. Squirt is built on a small scale with a physique vaguely resembling that of R2D2. His transparent head of smoked Plexiglas gives him an eerie, outer-space look that appeals to science-fiction fans; his small size appeals to youngsters. Years ago, Tom gave the first Squirt to his two young children, and they instantly fell in love with it. Colossus is more than 7 feet tall, so he towers over the people at a promotional event. Because of his size and his animated movements, spectators find that they cannot take their eyes off Colossus when he appears in public.

In February of 1983, I visited Tom Carroll and his wife, Sue, in their home in Long Beach, California. She told me that Tom has always been a creative "pack rat," with a talent for making something useful out of discards, surplus parts, and random junk. In his latest

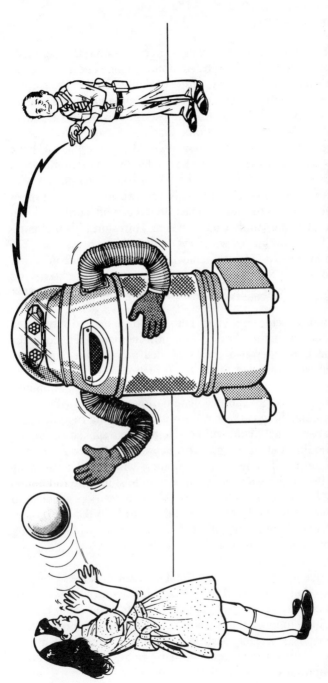

Radio-controlled promotional robots usually feature simple, rugged construction to help ensure reliability. The voice of the robot is transmitted to it by radio from the operator, who also controls its body movements by operating a hand-held transmitter. This model is the Squirt, built and marketed by Thomas Carroll of Universal Robot Systems in Long Beach, California. Children love to watch and touch the Squirt because it is built on such a small scale.

project, for instance, he is converting a large ultrasonic scanner made for hospital use into a sophisticated home robot. The instrument, which retailed for $70,000 new, cost Tom only $300 on the surplus market. It weighs 350 pounds, stands 6 feet high, and utilizes a large, vertical-axis arm which in medical use is positioned over the patient and locked in place for an ultrasonic diagnostic scan. "Most people would never be able to visualize how it could become the backbone of a robot," says his wife; but Tom has added two massive motors to allow his new "Ultra" robot to handle 50- to 100-pound objects with dexterity and precision—an unusually massive load for an experimental robot. Ultra is so strong, in fact, that it can lift Tom's children up to the roof of the family garage, where Tom stores his best paraphernalia. Ultra now bristles with rows of ultrasonic sensors, and Tom is planning to install a video camera with a small electronic memory, plus optical sensors to help the robot move around in the house and manipulate other devices such as electric can openers and push-button telephones.

A few months before my visit, Tom and his wife had remodeled some of the rooms in their home. Somehow he managed to convince her that the thing they had always needed most was a network of navigational wires installed under the carpeting to guide the movements of their household robots. By following the proper computer-activated wire, the robot can negotiate narrow doorways without the risk of paint-scratching contact. Colossus is still being modified, but when he is completed, Tom will be able to give a spoken command like "Go into the kitchen and get me a Pepsi," and Colossus will pass the request on to the household computer, which will respond by energizing the proper wires under the carpet to shunt the robot onto a trajectory leading to the refrigerator. Magnetic sensors attached to Colossus just above the level of the carpet will help the 225-pound robot traverse many different paths through the house without having to rely upon more complex and expensive sonar, visual, or tactile sensors.

Tom has one worrisome concern: "that the family cat doesn't decide to take a nap on top of one of the wires." He goes on to explain that "at high speeds, the robot's sensors may not detect the cat in time to prevent a painful robot–feline encounter." Colossus will also be rigged with infrared "heat-seeking" sensors to keep his directional microphone aimed at the warm bodies of human beings. This will cut down on background noise for easier voice recognition.

As Tom proudly points out, a few of the best promotional robots climbing down from today's drawing boards are rigged with features at least as impressive as those of the make-believe robots that starred in Hollywood films 20 years ago. Some respond to spoken commands; others converse with their owners. Speech-synthesis chips similar to the ones used in "Speak 'N Spell" toys and "talking" vending machines give the robot his own special electronic voice. Crude pattern-recognition techniques are also being introduced by hobbyists to enable their robots to negotiate unfamiliar terrain without mishap.

Some researchers have been experimenting with small radio transmitters to link mobile robots to a large modern computer. With this approach, the robot can be made to interact effectively with other household appliances such as dishwashers, closed-circuit television, and fire-warning systems. What will the robot of the future do if a fire suddenly starts in your house? It may smother the fire with a pillow, douse it with tap water, or sprinkle baking soda on it, then rush to the phone to call the local fire department—or your next-door neighbor. What will be his reaction if a burglar crashes through your patio window? Depending on your prearranged instructions, the robot may pull you out of bed, trip a silent alarm, or temporarily blind the intruder with a concentrated beam of light.

Today's unintelligent industrial manipulators are often regarded by amateur robotics researchers with thinly concealed disdain. Nor is the hobbyist always content with the "apparent" intelligence of promotional robots that derive their dexterity from remote-control radio links. Fortunately, new technologies may help raise the I.Q. of today's relatively unintelligent machines.

Ten years ago, reaching this lofty goal was beyond all reasonable hope. Of course, a brainy little machine named "Shakey" was waddling up and down the halls of the Stanford Research Institute searching for new problems to solve, and scientists at Johns Hopkins and M.I.T. were attempting to integrate mobile robots with digital computers. But building a robot that was flexible, mobile, and self-contained was essentially impracticable until the introduction of the microprocessor chip in 1972.

Microprocessors freed the robot from reliance upon clumsy electromechanical relays or hand-wired circuit boards. With a microprocessor, the robot's instructions can, instead, be placed in software (program commands). This makes its movements considerably more versatile and much easier to modify and refine. Surprisingly, one of the world's first microprocessor-controlled hobby robots was constructed by a New Jersey high school student named Todd Loofburrow in the late 1970s. With a little help from his father, Todd used a simple computer called the Commodore KIM-1 in building an impressive articulated mechanism which has brought him national recognition among hobbyists. Todd also wrote a fine book titled *How To Build a Computer-Controlled Robot*, in which he describes in detail the construction and the programming methods he used in building his machine.

James Hill of Covina, California, is representative of another breed of robotics experimenters. He has been building elaborate experimental robots for nearly 20 years, but he has no interest in producing robots for the commercial marketplace. Recently the creations of Jim and several other members of the International Robotics Foundation/ Robotics Experimenters' Amateur League (IRF/REAL) were featured on an ABC network news segment. Hill's robot "Charlie" was filmed as he dropped a bundle of trash into a garbage can—a slightly unpleasant but practical task for a hobby robot. Charlie's body slides up and down on a central stem with an elevatorlike movement which resembles that of the extraterrestrial in the Hollywood film *E.T.* Charlie's body stem also tilts forward to allow him to pick up objects lying on the floor.

"Jim Hill is not even an engineer," says Tom Carroll with a note of admiration in his voice, "but he has done things that amaze aerospace scientists." Impeccable craftsmanship went into the building of Charlie's intricate hands and arms, which bristle with electrical wires and hollow tubes. Many robot builders add decorative gingerbread just to make their creations seem more technical and scientific, but every part of Charlie is totally functional.

Jim Hill constructed his first robot 15 years ago. It had two movable legs, but its halting attempts at upright locomotion were a big disappointment. "I got it to walk," says Hill, "but the movement took up too much of its power." Although he propels himself on wheels instead of legs, Charlie is constructed in the typical humanoid form favored by Hollywood filmmakers. It took Hill four years to put Charlie together from aluminum sheet and square tubing. The final result is indisputably one of the most advanced hobby robots anywhere in the world, despite the fact that in constructing Charlie Jim Hill used only simple hand tools plus a saber saw, a hacksaw, and a workshop vise. Jim, who holds a routine job as a parts stocker for a car dealership, sees his robot as a lifelong labor of love. "The technology is changing so fast, Charlie will never be considered finished," he said recently.

No suitable vision system was available for his creation, so Jim meticulously designed and built one of his own—an elaborate electronic device that "uses a scanning light beam...to produce a three-dimensional picture in its head that lets it spot an object and determine how far away it is." Jim encountered similar difficulties when he tried to find an appropriate speech-recognition system on the commercial market; consequently, he is now busy working out his own unique design.

Although enthusiastic amateurs like Jim Hill and Tom Carroll are building some mighty impressive robots, the best and most intricate machines being used for public entertainment are the audioanimatronic characters on display at Disneyland, Walt Disney World, and Epcot Center. One of their most rousing routines involves the conflict between a shy industrial robot right off the assembly line and an egocentric audioanimatronic character with a long plastic beak. The show, which is located at Epcot Center in the Transportation Pavilion operated by General Motors, is called "The Robot and the Bird."

As the performance begins, the talkative bird is attempting to steal the spotlight while the silent but self-conscious robot is trying as best he can to hide from the spectators. Once he realizes there is no escape, he gradually warms up to the audience and puts together a credible routine for their edification and amusement. Among other things, he conducts an orchestral recording with a metal baton, spears an elusive doughnut, and removes various items of equipment from a circus trunk. The audience responds enthusiastically to his humanlike movements, which are all coordinated through conventional robotics programming techniques. Of course, this is not the first time the technicians in the Disney empire have entertained us with the delicate and precise movements of show robots. They have also given us such emotional performances as "Pirates of the Caribbean," "The Haunted Mansion," and "The Enchanted Tiki Room"—where even the flowers and the walls end up taking on a magic life of their own.

Like most industrial robots, audioanimatronic characters are usually immobile—although at the "Americana" exhibit in Epcot Center, Mark Twain and Benjamin Franklin seem to walk around freely and even climb a little flight of stairs! Clever technologies are used in controlling the gestures and other motions of the characters in the show. Both the background music and the voices of the characters are recorded on multichannel magnetic tapes alongside special, inaudible tones that trigger the various movements of each lifelike character. Every joint and facial feature is controlled by a specific, prearranged tone; the "muscles" of the character are actuated by compressed air flowing through hollow tubes in its body. The various discrete tones cause tiny valves to open or close on cue, thus swiveling a joint or inflating a flexible bladder to create a more subtle movement such as a change of facial expression. Every eye blink, every curled lip must be programmed by a skilled technician. Moreover, the patient craftsmen, who were referred to as "imagineers" by Walt Disney, must work their magic so that each movement fits the personality of the character in perfect synchronization with the music and the words.

The Disney empire is the best-known user of quality show robots—but surprisingly, the biggest users are pizza restaurants. Two major pizza chains, Pizza Time Theater and ShowBiz Place, have put large numbers of robots on their payrolls in an effort to capitalize on the 20-minute order cycle that creates customer boredom in many pizza parlors. The new pizza chains are using programmable robots to entertain their customers while they wait for their food to arrive. The restaurants are also lined with rows of video games—which are generating 25 percent of gross revenues and 40 to 50 percent of the profits. A restaurant equipped in this way is considerably larger than the traditional franchise pizza parlor of a few years ago, but it captures three or four times the sales and produces up to nine times the profits. If the current craze continues, each of the two major chains hopes to have in the neighborhood of 1,000 outlets by 1985, with eight to twelve robots working in each outlet. If these plans materialize on schedule, America will have more robots working in pizza parlors than in all the factories in our country combined.

Although both of the major chains feature rather corny routines, regular customers claim that the animation of ShowBiz is more diverting. Every few minutes, eight cheerful electronic animals perform skits and sing songs on three stages rimming the dining room. The motion and color fascinate young kids, who watch with open mouths. Some of the routines also intrigue their parents, especially the "Rock-Afire Explosion Band"—a gorilla, a bear, a mouse, and a dog—who do reasonably good imitations of the Beatles and the Beach Boys, two singing groups that were popular when the parents themselves were kids. The band shares center stage with Billy Bob, a southern redneck who exchanges wisecracks with his sidekick, a tipsy bird who makes gasohol and insists on sampling a little of it to make sure it is properly made.

Pizza Time's characters are a little less sophisticated. On one stage Chuck E. Cheese, "The New Joisey Rat," wisecracks with a droopy dog named Jasper T. Jowles, while elsewhere "Dolli Dimples," a buxom hippopotamus, moves her velour jowls and heaves her brocade bosom in time to torch songs, and nearby a Presley-esque dog swivels his furry hips to rock and roll.

The average family of four spends $22 to $24 during a 90-minute visit to one of the new pizza outlets, which, on the average, gross about $1.4 million per year—a take exceeding that of the typical McDonald's. Creative Engineering of Orlando, Florida, which makes many of the robots for use in pizza restaurants, currently produces 120 units per year with a staff of about 200.

Other restaurant chains are also getting into the act. One features Looney Tunes characters such as Daffy Duck, Bugs Bunny, and Porky Pig. Robots are cheap help that bring in customers and get them in the mood to spend more freely; but some observers are beginning to wonder if the public may be approaching saturation.

CHAPTER 9

HOW TO BUILD YOUR OWN ROBOT

Congratulations! It's been nine exhausting months since you began your pet project. In the meantime, your other hobbies and interests have all melted away, and an army of hungry divorce lawyers are standing outside pounding on your door. Building a robot was harder than you ever thought possible, and you've lost maybe 30 pounds. But finally, the last few components are firmly bolted in place, and it's time to take your creation outside for his first leisurely stroll. Your neighbors are surprised to see your robot—and also his beaming owner, because you never venture out anymore. Swarms of lively kids gang around touching, teasing, fondling the funny little machine.

If you've done your homework properly, your creation is a genuine work of art worthy of a prize for engineering excellence. A few people have met him already, but his official debut will take place in your home at a small dinner party for fifty. (Well, it started out small!) Your guests have all busied themselves with new party games like spilling tall glasses of cheap Chablis on your favorite Oriental rug and hiding stale potato chips in the soil under your house plants. Suddenly, you motion for silence, because your robot's voice-recognition unit is so easily confused by background noise. "Rover," you call out. The closet doors in the hall swing open and out rolls your pride-and-joy.

"Did you call, master?"

You cringe a little when you hear the words. "I've got to reprogram that voice response," you tell your guests sheepishly; "I sound like a slave owner." Rover glides across the room over to the buffet, artfully dodging furniture and guests. "Potato chips, sandwiches, or punch?" he asks in a soothing baritone voice. When he speaks, the room falls silent as your relatives and friends stand around the punch bowl with their faces hanging out.

When Rover has finished serving the hors d'oeuvres, he scoops up an armload of cups and saucers and deposits them in the dishwasher. He then glides silently back into the hall closet. "I must relax now and recharge my batteries," he tells the crowd just before he disappears; "tomorrow I have a heavy date with a water cooler."

Well-wishers from the office gather around in a tight cluster as you explain how you spent the past nine months sequestered in your house. "I made the master templates and fabricated my own fiberglass body shell," you tell them, casually, "because nothing readymade was suitable for the robot I had in mind." You go on to describe the endless hours of machine-shop work that went into your creation's intricate arms and hands.

It was a tiring ordeal, but now it's your turn to be lazy. With simple voice commands, you can get your robot to answer the door, take out the trash, or call your friends on the phone and talk to them using his artificial voice. Other spoken commands instruct him to operate your kitchen appliances, your security devices, and your stereo cassette recorder. Lately you have been toying with new plans for turning him into a yard-maintenance robot. "He could mow the lawn and trim the shrubs by following metal cables buried under the grass," you tell your guests, trying not to sound as excited as you feel. "After that I plan to teach him how to cook and sew."

Does this account seem just a little fanciful? Of course it does. But if you have been following recent developments in hobby robotics, you know that household robots may eventually become a real possibility. Exciting new developments have been taking place in computer programming, artificial intelligence, pattern recognition, video communication, and a host of other engineering disciplines. If you are planning a major robotics project, you will need a working knowledge of these varied disciplines plus a great deal of cash. Depending on your goals, your robot could end up with an equivalent value approaching $100,000. Of course, your actual out-of-pocket expenses will be a good deal less, because most of the labor will be your own and you will scrounge around to locate secondhand and surplus parts.

If your ambitions lie at the opposite end of the spectrum, you can, with moderate expertise, build a remarkably inexpensive working robot. A surplus house in Philadelphia, Herbach & Rademan, provides a simple robot kit for about $50. The finished product resembles a small mechanical turtle named "Herbug." Another way to get started in hobby robotics is to build a small motorized platform from surplus parts. If you enjoy fiddling with your creation, you can add a few switches and relays to increase its flexibility and control.

Here's an example of such a low-cost construction. You can buy

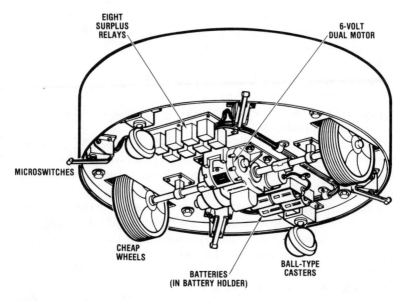

In your spare time you can construct a battery-powered dishpan robot from secondhand parts for about $20. It uses microswitches to detect barriers in its way and surplus relays to determine the proper response. Power is supplied by a reversible motor of the type found in simple children's toys. Although the robot may seem complicated in this sketch, it is possible to construct it using ordinary tools in a few dozen hours of patient labor.

TYPICAL TABLETOP TRAJECTORY

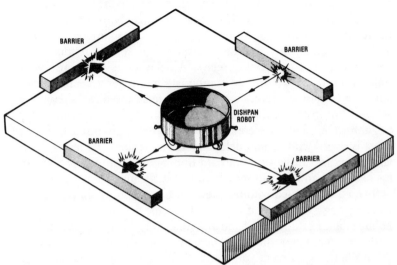

When the dishpan robot hits a barrier, it will automatically back up or change direction to trace out convoluted trajectories on your kitchen table. You can bring about interesting changes in the robot's behavior by rewiring its electro-mechanical relays and microswitches. It even goes through behavior patterns that seem to exhibit free will.

a dual reversible electric motor of the type used in children's toys for under $5. Herbach & Rademan is one popular source of supply. Now attach two wheels at a cost of $2 each. Mount motor and wheels on a $1 metal dishpan and add a $2 caster for balance. So far you have spent $12. Add four 50-cent surplus microswitches around the rim of the dishpan for object detection and a $1 battery holder containing four 50-cent flashlight batteries. Now attach four surplus 6-volt relays at $1 each. Congratulations! You are now the proud owner of a working robot. It cost about $20.

You can "teach" your dishpan robot to do fancy tricks by wiring its relays together in various patterns. For example, you can rig the wires so that if the microswitch mounted on the front of the robot touches an object, its motor will reverse, causing it to back up. If it hits another object while it is moving backward, the microswitch on the back will cause it to activate a single wheel, thus making it turn in a gentle circle. Similar switches mounted on the sides of the pan can be rigged to activate the other relays to produce similar responses.

The simple, preprogrammed movements of your dishpan robot may eventually begin to seem a little routine. Fortunately, you can increase his repertoire of turns and pirouettes by adding additional switches and relays, and you can achieve even greater artistic pizzazz with delay timers and sequencing relays. A delay timer will cause your robot to begin to execute the appropriate maneuver several seconds after the triggering event. A sequencing relay produces alternating actions. For instance, the first time the relay is triggered, your robot might turn left, but the second time he will turn right instead. If your robot is rigged with several delay timers and sequencing relays, your family and friends will have a hard time figuring out the patterns of his behavior, and he will seem almost like an intelligent entity.

If you are intrigued with the clever antics of your mobile dishpan, you may being to wonder if you could become the owner of a genuine hobby robot. Fortunately, if you are sufficiently dedicated, robot ownership is a realistic possibility. There are basically three legal ways to get a robot of your own: you can buy one fully assembled, or in kit form; you can get a set of plans from a knowledgeable expert and build a duplicate version; or you can plan and construct your own one-of-a-kind original design.

The easiest route to robot ownership is to buy one ready-made from any of several different manufacturers, available in several different price ranges. Toys "R" Us markets the Armatron robot (actually a teleoperator) for about $60. A classier unit is available from Neiman-Marcus, which began advertising a "Domestic Robot System" in its Christmas catalog in 1981. According to its marketeers it can, among other things, "open the doors, take out the trash, bring in the paper, sweep the floor, water the plants, dust the furniture, pick up after the children, and pour the wine." The deluxe model includes color TV and AM/FM stereo. Feeling lonesome? The catalog also includes detailed descriptions of a cuddly pet robot named "Wires." Other personal models resemble industrial robots in form and function; they are usually immobile, and in general, they feature only one articulated arm. Mitsubishi, Microbot, and Sandhu all produce fully assembled experimental robots; however, the most exciting new model comes from Heath, the maker of Heathkits.

After years of persistent rumors, the Heath Company's Hero-I (*Heath Educational Robot*) finally made its debut in the Christmas season of 1982. At $1,500 in kit form, Hero-I is relatively expensive, but its

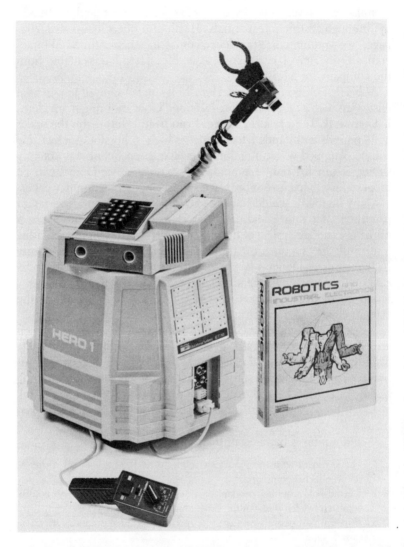

The Heath HERO I Robot (Model ET18) is the most advanced and versatile product for teaching and learning robotics available on the market today. Its companion Robotics Education Course, the first of its kind ever developed, provides a comprehensive grounding in robot technology.

manufacturer is well known and respected for excellent products backed by thorough instruction manuals. Heath also offers a superb 1,200-page, two-volume correspondence course in robotics for $100 to accompany its Hero-I kit. A fully assembled Hero-I is available from the company for $2,500.

At his first press conference, Hero-I ingratiated himself to potential customers with a crowd-pleasing greeting: "Good morning. I am Hero-I. I can walk. I can talk. I can see. I can hear." Hero-I tips the scales at 39 pounds and stands 1 foot 8 inches high in his stocking feet. He can be equipped with an optional clawlike gripper, but it is not very strong; it can lift only 1 pound, which means that Hero-I can be programmed to fetch your bedroom slippers but not the Sunday paper.

Many hobbyists would have preferred a visually interesting design patterned after movie androids, but Hero-I is, in fact, more like a miniature mobile replica of his bigger brothers found on the assembly line. Still, he is a surprisingly sophisticated and versatile machine. In the words of Douglas Bonham, director of Heathkit/Zenith Educational Systems, "The Heath robot incorporates all the basic systems found on modern industrial robots, plus a few that are still in the experimental stage of industrial application."

A special microprocessor chip controls the robot's movements, which are powered by eight electrical motors driven by four rechargeable batteries. His manipulator claw can be programmed to grasp and lift small objects, and he can speak single words or whole sentences using his optional speech-synthesizer device. A built-in electronic clock fosters the convenient use of time-programmable "wake-up" commands.

Programming is handled in three different ways:

1. The keyboard atop the robot's swiveling turret head allows his owner to key in selected commands.
2. A hand-held teaching pendant provides for precise and easy path control with step-by-step push-button programming.
3. A special port permits easy entry of more complicated programs stored on cassette tapes.

Hero-I is the most challenging kit Heath has ever marketed to the general public. Because of its complexity, company spokesmen do not recommend it as your first Heathkit assembly project. In their opinion, anyone who attempts assembly should first take the company's special robotics course, even though this is not absolutely necessary.

Another major source of modern instructional robots is the Microbot Corporation of Mountain View, California. Microbot markets the "Minimover 5" and the new "Teachmover." These are not kits; they are preassembled robot arms that can be connected to almost any computer, including inexpensive personal microcomputers such as the TRS-80 made by Radio Shack or the Apple II. The Minimover 5 was one of the first experimental robots made available to the general public. Dozens of private companies and universities have adapted its cleverly articulated arm to their existing systems.

A newcomer to the educational-robot field is the Mitsubishi "Move Master" marketed by E&L Instruments. This hobby robot bears a strong physical resemblance to Microbot's Teachmover. With its onboard Z-80 Central Processing Unit, the Move Master can be adapted for control by an Apple computer or an even simpler microcomputer such as Rockwell International's AIM-65 or the Fox made by E&L Instruments. Despite its sluggish movements and its slavish resemblance to its rivals from Microbot, the Move Master is a well-constructed and relatively precise manipulator device.

If you decide to build your own hobby robot by following the plans developed by a knowledgeable expert in the field, you will have a good chance of completing the project in a reasonable amount of time; but you will probably not end up expressing your own individuality as well as you could if you chose to build a new creation in accordance with your own custom design. Still, if you are a newcomer to hobby robotics, adopting a proved design may be a reasonable compromise way to get started.

A few years ago *Radio Electronics* ran a ten-article series on the construction of the "Unicorn 1," a simple hobby robot. Dozens of copies were built successfully, and several more are in various stages of completion. Many other hobbyists read and followed David Heiserman's *Build Your Own Working Robot*, in which he describes how to make a duplicate of his brainchild called "Buster," a fascinating machine with an animal-like reflex system which, among other things, causes Buster to "run around the floor, poking into corners and crying woefully whenever its batteries run low."

Buster is so constructed that he has a primitive form of free will—an unusual attribute for a hobby robot. Heiserman characterizes him as "a machine that is capable of setting his own goals and achieving them within the limitations of his own logical and physical abilities." He goes on to add that "Buster can interact with a human operator,

This Mitsubishi Move Master RM-101 has been programmed to depress the keys on a microcomputer with a wooden pencil. The Move Master features precise five-axis control for meaningful demonstrations of robotics techniques in industrial and classroom settings. Although its movements are fairly precise, the Move Master is a heavy, sluggish machine.

provided he doesn't have any other needs that are more urgent at the time."

While philosophy professors have been preoccupied with disagreements on the concept of free will and individual choice, David Heiserman has been putting together metal and electronics to explore the logical consequences of this esoteric debate. Of what use is a machine like Buster? Heiserman has asked himself the same question, but in recent years he has concluded that this is a fruitless line of investigation. "The question is not really appropriate," he writes. "It's like asking what use is a puppy."

The construction of a Buster robot is divided into three separate evolutionary phases. In the first phase his name is "Buster I," and he is primarily "a wheeled machine that can be driven and steered by means of a simple control panel." He moves in forward and reverse at different speeds. He can also be turned left and right at two different angles.

In the second phase of his construction, when he is rigged with the capacity for making simple logical decisions, the robot is renamed "Buster II." He is also given a set of touch sensors at this stage and "a control system that lets him make an appropriate motion reflex whenever he blunders into a solid object." Moreover, Buster II can sense when his battery is running low, and he learns to sound an alarm if he becomes trapped between two objects.

"Buster III," who emerges in the third phase of construction, has active goal-seeking capabilities, which, for example, allow him to track down a target object. For instance, if his battery power diminishes below a certain level, he will automatically seek out his battery charger and plug himself in to reenergize his systems. When his batteries are recharged, he backs up and continues his feverish goal-directed activities. Buster III can be controlled to some extent, but his survival instincts are so strong that he "always retains his reflex capability that overrides just about anything his master tells him to do."

If your interest lies specifically in the construction of a show robot for promotional purposes, you may want to contact Jerry Rebman of Houston, Texas. Jerry is an interesting, knowledgeable fellow who offers an instruction manual on how to build your own "Garcan." Garcan is an armless robot whose body is a 30-gallon garbage can. Jerry furnishes plans, schematics, and an extensive parts list to help you complete your project. If you are unable to find a particular part locally, Jerry Rebman will sell it to you. His instruction manual also tells you how to install a number of imaginative robot gimmicks such as smoke bombs and sirens. If you would like to buy a fully assembled duplicate of Garcan, Jerry will build it for you to your specifications for about $4,000.

If you plan to design and build your own original robot, you will need a good mechanical background coupled with a working knowledge of electronics. As the brains behind a major new robot, you have open to you two design philosophies:

1. You can put together a simple, workable device, then make gradual improvements to it.
2. You can develop a single overall design, then execute it all at once.

If you choose the second approach, you will need to have all aspects of your robot in mind from the start. This will probably result in a more efficient construction and improved placement of components; but bear in mind that until your robot is completed, you will not be able to use it to amaze and confound your friends and neighbors. In other words, you will reap none of the benefits from your time, labor, and cash until you have completed the entire project—which may require months, or years.

Before you undertake the construction of a major robot, read up on the subject as much as you can and think seriously about your robot's ultimate use. A simple household model such as the radio-controlled version of the Squirt as designed by Universal Robots should present no insurmountable design or construction problems for the beginner. When finished, it will be able to do a few useful things such as serving drinks, answering the door, and entertaining your guests with endearing mannerisms.

When you begin to sketch the overall design of your robot, choose its body dimensions carefully so that it will be able to pass easily through your halls and doorways. Be mindful of the placement of the furniture and other obstacles in your house. Overhanging surfaces such as tabletops can be especially bothersome, because they may strike the upper body of your robot while escaping detection by its floor-level sensors. Padded bumpers attached to your creation at appropriate locations can help protect valuable items of furniture from nicks and dents, and small pads or rollers mounted on your walls can help minimize scratches.

Doorway sizes, turning radii, and carpet types require especially

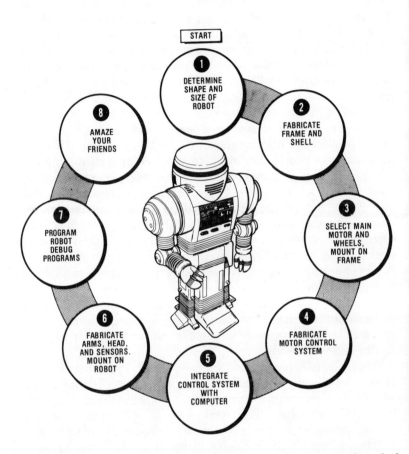

This diagram illustrates some of the major steps you will need to go through if you decide to put together your own hobby or promotional robot. Steps 5 and 7, in which you integrate the control system with the other hardware elements and debug your control program, are likely to be the hardest tasks you will encounter. Step 8 is definitely the most fun.

careful consideration. If your robot will have to negotiate stairs, your problems will multiply, but not to an insurmountable degree. In 1981, Marty Weinstein wrote a book titled *Android Design* in which he described a robot mounted on tractor treads capable of climbing stairs.

You will probably want to start with a simple robot equipped with relay switches, only later adding or substituting more sophisticated computer control. If you adopt this approach, leave enough room inside for the later installation of the microcomputer, and be sure to choose electrical motors that can be controlled by digital pulses. Your robot will need on-board sensors so that its computer "brain" will know where its body is positioned and how its arms are oriented. Shaft encoders can help the robot monitor the precision of his own movements so that he can, for example, pick up a small object or find his way through a narrow doorway. A shaft encoder is a precisely constructed disk with a series of open slots punched around its perimeter. As the disk rotates, a stationary light beam shines through the slots one by one. The frequency with which the light beam is interrupted is proportional to the rotational speed of the disk. This information allows the robot to fine-tune his own movements automatically. A potentiometer is an alternative choice for precision control. Its operation is similar to that of the volume-control unit on a portable radio. As the shaft of the potentiometer rotates, a metal strip moves along a resistance element to cause changes in voltage which, in turn, give the robot the necessary information on how his body parts are twisted and positioned.

So far, you have formulated a general plan for developing the shape of your robot and for selecting his internal sensors. The next thing you need to do is design the power source and select the main motors. In general, robots that walk on two legs are still in the realm of science fiction, although a few successful models have been built with larger numbers of legs. Beetle-like designs with six legs have turned out to be surprisingly efficient and stable even when they are walking across rough terrain. An excellent description of walking machines was published in the January 1983 issue of *Scientific American*. Of course, the devices described in the article are still in their infancy, so you should probably settle for much simpler wheels or tractor treads for the locomotion of your robot. Tractor treads are difficult to steer, especially if they are to be operated on uneven carpets; for this reason, hobby robots usually travel about on motor-driven wheels.

Most radio-controlled promotional robots are designed with two

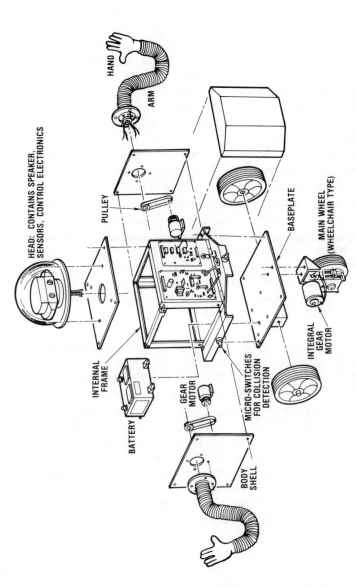

HEAD: CONTAINS SPEAKER, SENSORS, CONTROL ELECTRONICS

HAND

ARM

PULLEY

BASEPLATE

MAIN WHEEL (WHEELCHAIR TYPE)

INTERNAL FRAME

BATTERY

GEAR MOTOR

MICRO-SWITCHES FOR COLLISION DETECTION

INTEGRAL GEAR MOTOR

BODY SHELL

Some of the major components of a typical hobby robot are sketched in this exploded view. This particular model uses wheelchair wheels powered by a 12-volt car battery. The robot's arms are corrugated plastic tubing, and its head is a translucent Plexiglas globe. Microswitches line the lower edges of the robot to minimize damage from contact with walls and other barriers.

independently side-driven wheels plus idler wheels or casters on the front and back for balance. Tom Carroll uses this arrangement on his Squirt-series robots. A robot built in this way is easily adapted to radio control, and it can turn a full 360 degrees within its own axis. A second wheel arrangement utilizes either one or two separate steering wheels in addition to the wheels carrying most of the load. A third uses a single front motor-driven wheel which doubles as the steering wheel. This technique, which is best suited to robots utilizing computerized control, was employed by Todd Loofburrow in building his "Mike" robot.

Almost all hobby robots are battery-powered. Many use ordinary car batteries, which produce a great deal of power per pound at a reasonable cost. Unfortunately, if your robot is accidentally tipped over, the liquid electrolyte in the car battery may eat right through his body and your floor. Jellied-electrolyte batteries are spillproof, but rather expensive. Smaller robots sometimes use motorcycle batteries or nickel-cadmium batteries, which are powerful and safe, but extremely expensive for the small amount of power they deliver.

The major movements of a robot are powered by its main motor. If your robot is big and heavy, an electric wheelchair motor could be an excellent choice. Wheelchair motors are rugged and powerful for their size and weight. Several nice models are provided by Everest & Jennings, and the British firm A-BEC produces a well-designed wheelchair motor that is used in Android Amusement's Drink Caddy 2 and Universal Robot's Colossus. The retail price for a set of two motors is about $450, so you should try to find them at secondhand or surplus-parts stores. Another popular choice, which has been used with great success by many robot builders, is the 6-volt Mabuchi RS-85 permanent-magnet motor. Unfortunately, this model is becoming harder and harder to find, and it can be fried by a 12-volt power supply. Surplus 12-volt bicycle-assist motors are another excellent selection, although they must be geared down for use in robots.

Now that you have a basic robot frame rigged with a motor and a battery, you will need to select the preferred method of robot control. A promotional robot usually gets its control signals from a nearby human operator, who transmits them to an on-board radio receiver. Proportional control in both forward and reverse is provided by "electronic throttles" made by both Vantec and Futaba. Contact your local hobby shop to see what it has in stock.

If you opt for computer control, you will need to install devices in your robot that respond to electrical pulses. A stepper motor is one popular approach. Most motors rotate smoothly through many revolutions even if they receive only a short burst of power. By contrast, if you send a short pulse to a stepper motor, its rotor will turn only a small fraction of a revolution. The on-board computer might, for example, send 240 pulses to each of the two wheel motors to cause the robot to move forward exactly one foot. Similarly, 600 pulses routed to an arm motor might swivel the joint 60 degrees in response to the computer's command. Verification that the robot has reached the proper location or the proper speed can be provided internally by tachometers or shaft encoders. The pulses sent back from one of these devices might tell the computer, in effect, "Yes, my left arm has swiveled sixty degrees" or "I am moving forward at a rate of two feet per second."

As your design begins to get firmer, you will need to select your robot's computer. The Commodore KIM-1 is no longer being produced, but Rockwell's new AIM-65 is a good low-cost selection. For less than $500 you can get a typewriter-style keyboard, an LED display, and a 20-column printer. Other single-board computers such as the SYM-1 and Micro Professor are alternative choices, or you can select one of the newer models such as the Motorola 68000. These products are all supported by solid manuals and other documentation.

If he is to respond to his environment, your robot must be equipped with sensors. Sonar ranging is one proved way to detect solid objects at a distance. Polaroid produces a fine experimental kit for $150 that will help you learn all you need to know about sonar ranging for robots. The Polaroid ranging device can detect objects or barriers as close as 10 inches or as far away as 35 feet. Once you have the basic system installed in your robot, extra sonar ranging devices aimed in a different direction will cost only about $30 each. Surplus-parts houses are a good source of inexpensive sonar and ultrasonic ranging equipment. Optical sensors and video cameras can also be used to detect objects, and infrared and magnetic-path detectors can be used for trajectory control.

By now your robot should be developing his own personality, so you will no doubt want to equip him with his own arms and hands and possibly a swiveling, turret-style head. Simple claws on nonarticulated arms will suffice for some simple purposes, but your ambitions may dictate multijointed hands with three or five fingers each. Manipulator construction is tricky. Start with simple concepts and work toward a more complex design.

At this point, you should have a robot that can do a few impressive things. But you still need to program him, which may turn out to be surprisingly tedious. A new computer program is almost always plagued with bugs and glitches, and when it is driving a robot, the problems are greatly magnified. No matter how much care is exercised, motors and feedback control devices always seem to get wired backward. If this happens to you, watch out! When the power is applied, your brainchild may suddenly leap off the workbench and smash himself on the floor. Gene Oldfield, the brains behind a company called "Robot Repair" in Sacramento, California, has often wondered why robot programming is so extraordinarily difficult. "I have often spent two or three hours at the keyboard," he says, "only to find that I've completed just eighteen program steps, and those steps make the robot do things I don't want it to." Even if you know computer programming fairly well, count on several weeks to program your robot to carry out even the simplest tasks.

Showmanship gimmicks add spice and excitement to the antics of a hobby robot. High-intensity strobe lights, smoke-detection alarms, and infrared intrusion detectors are common examples. Others include pump-driven squirting flowers, model-railroad smoke generators, radio-controlled tape decks, clanging bells, beeping horns, flashing lights, and business-card dispensers. Some of the more elaborate promotional robots are rigged with small color television cameras to record the behavior of the people around them and video cassette recorders to play commercial messages on special chest-mounted monitors. A few of them, including the DC-2, are rigged with dedicated microcomputers so that spectators can challenge the robot to play video games.

Robots can "speak" to their companions using voice synthesizers, electronic devices that employ a special Read Only Memory (ROM) chip coupled with a synthesizer chip to mimic the human voice. A speech synthesizer works with phonemes, primitive units of sound such as "ah" and "oh," which can be strung together in sequence to produce realistic (or at least recognizable) spoken words. Another popular type of speech synthesizer uses actual words and sentences previously recorded by a human being.

Some hobby robots respond appropriately to commands issued by their owners—or other people who have taken the trouble to learn their special language. Speech recognition is accomplished by a computer program that searches out meaningful patterns in the sounds of spoken words. Most speech-recognition units now on the market must be trained to recognize the utterances of a specific individual. The characteristics of the spoken words are stored in the computer as special templates. When new words are spoken, they are compared electronically with the templates in the computer's memory. The comparisons are made by a microprocessor which automatically determines if there is an acceptable match. Although speech recognition is impressive, it is a specialized capability. Consequently, you may want to wait until your robot's other subsystems are operating properly before you attempt to include it in your creation's repertoire of robot gimmicks.

Robotics research tends to be a solitary undertaking involving long hours of hard work. Fortunately, in recent years hobby robotics experimenters have begun to band together in clubs so they can pool their knowledge and experience and socialize with their colleagues. One of the first organizations of this type, the United States Robotics Society, was formed in the mid-1970s in Albuquerque, New Mexico. Later it was moved to the San Francisco area. Unfortunately, as is so often the case with small, volunteer organizations, the U.S. Robotics Society has encountered organizational problems and is now temporarily inactive. A similar group, the International Institute of Robotics, was formed about the same time in Pelahatchee, Mississippi, and its organizers offered the first robotics courses for the hobbyist. This organization has also become inactive, but now that new interest in robotics is being aroused, it may soon become active again.

In the late '70s, a new magazine, *Robotics Age*, was started to help meet the needs of those who were developing an interest in robotics. In the summer of 1980, the International Robotics Foundation (IRF) was formed under the auspices of *Robotics Age*. The following year the IRF became a separate entity. Tom Carroll was the founding president of the organization, which is now based in Seal Beach, California. John Gutman of the Atlanta Computer Society has worked with Tom Carroll and Ted Blank of the Boston Computer Society to form a stronger robotics experimenters group called the Robot Experimenters Amateur League (REAL). The main goal of REAL is to spread the word to the general public that manlike robots are indeed "real" and not just fanciful creatures springing from the minds of science-fiction writers.

The highly capable household robot that was described at the beginning of this chapter does not yet exist; but most of the things he was described as doing are possible, at least in primitive form, with today's technology. Perhaps you will end up building such a robot. If you do accept the challenge, many people will be willing to assist you and give you useful information. The Appendix lists helpful sources of parts and information.

The robot-building boom is on. Magazines, newspapers, and television talk shows are all giving broad coverage to the robot revolution—which has also made the cover of *Time* magazine. If you would like to get involved in this exciting revolution, you were lucky enough to be born at the right time.

CHAPTER 10

ROBOTS FOR THE FUTURE

In this final chapter of *The Robot Revolution* we will engage in a few gutsy speculations concerning the future of robotics. We begin with an examination of the space-based defensive system recently proposed by the Reagan Administration, then move on to other types of robots now being planned for use in space and on the floor of the ocean. We will also examine the amazing capabilities of the six-legged "Functionoid" robot recently tested by researchers at Odetics, a small aerospace-equipment manufacturer located on the West Coast. After that we briefly examine two methods whereby the human body itself can be converted into a kind of robot. The final paragraphs of this chapter consider special "vacation" robots that could make some kinds of foreign travel unnecessary, and subminiature robots capable of entering the human body and performing delicate surgery—from the inside!

In March of 1983, in an address carried by all three television networks, President Reagan caught his audience (and some of his advisers) by surprise when he unveiled a futuristic plan for nullifying the destructive power of the Soviet Union's nuclear-tipped intercontinental ballistic missiles. His proposal called for the construction of hundreds of "intelligent" robot battle stations to form a multilayered defense in outer space to shield the United States and her allies against a sneak attack. At one point the President spoke directly to his military researchers, urging them to provide the technological impetus to back up his concept for ensuring the survival of the American way of life: "I call upon the scientific community in our country, those who gave us the nuclear weapons, to turn their great talents now to the cause of mankind and world peace, to give us the means of rendering those nuclear weapons impotent and obsolete."

There were, of course, negative reactions to the President's novel approach to national defense. Many of his sternest critics thought he was grasping for a bargaining chip in future arms-reduction talks with the Russians. Others regarded his proposal as a transparent trick motivated by partisan politics. House Armed Services Committee member Les Aspin, for instance, dismissed the entire concept as "part Democrat bashing, part *Star Wars*." Many members of the President's own political party exhibited a lack of enthusiasm for the idea of a space-based ballistic-missile defense. For instance, Representative Jim Leach, a moderate Republican, expressed fears that research into the possibilities for military laser battle stations might preclude meaningful arms-control negotiations. He was also skeptical about the practicality of the President's scheme, suggesting that it was "fallacious to assume . . . that scientists can somehow develop new technologies to render harmless the awesome weapons twentieth-century research has wrought."

Months before the speech, another expert on military technology in the Reagan camp had advanced the opinion that laser weapons were a highly questionable means of defending our country against enemy missiles. In a widely quoted magazine interview, he contended that "The high-energy laser is to warfare what Laetrile is to cancer."

Nevertheless, a few days after the broadcast, *Time* magazine writer Frederic Golden set forth an unusually clear account of how the robot system envisioned by the President might achieve a viable defense against nuclear annihilation:

> Imagine a nuclear-tipped missile rising from a silo deep inside the Soviet Union, fixed on a target in the U.S. Almost immediately its fiery exhaust plumes trip warning sensors in satellites orbiting overhead. One of those

satellites sends a powerful beam of light, or perhaps even a cascade of subatomic particles, bursting down from the heavens like a Jovian lightning bolt. The beam homes in on the ascending missile and fastens onto its nose cone. Burning through, the beam turns the electronic guidance system into silicon mush, sending the missile wobbling off course and totally immobilizing its nuclear warhead.

At first thought, an effective space-based defense against a storm of nuclear warheads raining down on our country may seem like an entirely impractical pipe dream. All the President is asking America's engineers to provide is a powerful fleet of orbiting battle stations sweeping repeatedly across the sky always ready, at a moment's notice, to shoot down hundreds or thousands of enemy missiles in flight, each tracing out a different trajectory and each swooping down toward a different terrestrial target at a speed of something like 15,000 miles per hour—or roughly ten times the muzzle velocity of a .22 rifle bullet. Moreover, if it occurs at all, the attack will likely involve intense salvos of military missiles launched in waves purposely concentrated in time and place to overwhelm the defense. Consequently, the defenders must be extraordinarily agile, having only a few seconds at most, to finish off one missile before attacking another. Most schemes call for the destruction of the missiles within the first 8 minutes after lift-off, while they still contain explosive propellants and before they have released their heat-resistant warheads. If this approach is adopted, the defenders in space will have to be capable of rapidly making intelligent decisions in response to situations they have never faced before.

If an engineering solution exists at all, it will probably consist of rigging the defenders to fire "bullets" that travel several times faster than their targets, preferably along simple, predictable trajectories. Laser beams are an excellent candidate because they move in straight lines at the speed of light, they can be turned on and off rapidly, and they can be pointed toward a new target in an instant. A laser beam is a pencil-thin stripe of monochromatic light (electromagnetic radiation) in which all the waves march along in a coherent pattern. Such a beam travels at the speed of light—669.6 million miles an hour, or about 50,000 times as fast as the enemy's swiftest intercontinental ballistic missile. Because of its rapid speed, there is no possibility of outrunning or evading the beam from a laser, assuming that the laser is accurately pointed toward its target.

The energy in a laser is focused on its target by a large concave mirror, similar in shape to the inside surface of an automobile headlight. Mirrors ground with the necessary level of precision are difficult to produce and maintain. The required pointing accuracies also present formidable engineering difficulties. The laser must be directed toward targets thousands of miles away with pinpoint precision; the slightest deviation may cause its beam to miss its target and pass harmlessly into space. Downing a missile with a laser beam is roughly equivalent to hitting a dime with a rifle bullet from a distance of 5 miles. One promising approach uses a feedback control system in which the laser battle station senses the laser light reflected from the target. This allows it to make extremely fine adjustments in pointing.

Still, achieving the required level of accuracy is not unprecedented. NASA's large space telescope, soon to be launched into orbit aboard the Space Shuttle, will have even more stringent requirements for accurate pointing and tracking. However, the space telescope, when ordered to focus its attention on a new heavenly body, will have several hours or even days to swivel to a new orientation and settle into the required alignment. The laser battle station will have to redirect its beam within seconds; otherwise some of the enemy missiles will pass beyond the horizon before they can be destroyed.

In a typical defensive system, several hundred laser battle stations will be positioned in low-altitude orbits about 400 miles above the earth. Each will be a highly responsive robot with a single deadly mission: to wipe out enemy missiles. Most of the time, the defenders will sweep across the sky staring downward, looking for moving targets and intense sources of heat such as the exhaust produced by a salvo of rockets. Detection will be accomplished with acutely sensitive "eyes" (infrared sensors and optical telescopes). Surveillance responsibilities will be shared with a variety of other orbiting satellites and sensors located on the ground in protected sanctuaries. All the hardware elements in the network—laser battle stations, ground-based sensors, orbiting detectors—will exchange information continuously, much of it relayed through dedicated communication satellites hovering high above the battleground in geosynchronous orbits.

The command to begin the battle will probably be under ground control, but artificial-intelligence routines programmed into the computers carried aboard the laser battle stations will help them decide what to do in any particular situation—when to attack, when to back off, when to wait for more complete information. If the need arises, actuators will automatically swivel the spacecraft to provide its sensors with a better view of any suspicious-looking targets. Other precision actuators will make constant adjustments to the curvature of the large mirrors to maintain precisely the right shape. If the battle station itself comes under attack, its computer will command it to turn its most rugged side toward the attackers or fire its laser to knock them out of the sky. Other methods of self-defense may include radar-reflective chaff, explosive warheads, and killer satellites flying in tight formation with the battle stations. In a warfare situation, the battle stations will exchange observations and battle plans to ensure that they do not attack the same targets.

Ordinary sources of illumination—the sun, incandescent light bulbs, birthday candles—emit *incoherent* waves of light which vary randomly in time, direction, and frequency. Their wave patterns are analogous to the irregular wavelets produced by random drops of rain falling on a mud puddle. By contrast, a laser produces *coherent* waves similar to the regularly spaced, parallel water waves being driven by a uniform wind. Laser light is an intense pencil-thin beam of parallel waves all sharing the same frequency, with coincident peaks and troughs.

Of course, the beams produced by ordinary lasers are much too tenuous to damage a military missile in flight. Two modern types of laser are currently favored by engineers for generating the fierce levels of power needed to achieve the ambitious goal: *chemical lasers* and *nuclear-pumped X-ray lasers*. In most cases, the lasing medium and the energy source are separate entities; but in a chemical laser, the chemicals being burned to provide energy also serve as the basic lasing material. Like a rocket engine, a chemical laser burns a mixture of fuel and oxidizer. Liquefied hydrogen and fluorine, two savagely energetic elements, are one combination favored for space defense applications.

The nuclear-pumped X-ray laser produces its lasing energy in an unusual way; it detonates a small nuclear weapon inside a rugged containment vessel. The vessel is rimmed with as many as 50 space-age "beanshooters"—thin metal tubes each of which blasts out an intense beam of X-ray laser energy in a particular direction. The energy emanating from each tube can fry an enemy missile within seconds. Immediately before the nuclear weapon is detonated, a computer on board the laser battle station points each of its individual tubes toward one of the enemy missiles.

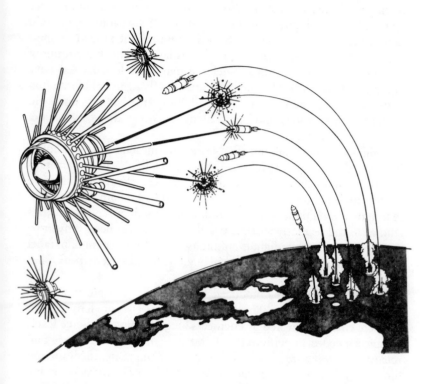

In theory, a few hundred nuclear-powered laser battle stations like these could provide an impenetrable barrier to shield the United States and its allies against an attack by the enemy's nuclear-tipped ballistic missiles. When the sensors aboard the battle station or those on nearby surveillance satellites detect a salvo of missiles launched from enemy territory, the battle-station computer commands each hollow lasing rod to point toward an incoming missile. A nuclear weapon inside the metal body of the spacecraft is then detonated to create deadly laser beams streaming from each tube to down the enemy missiles. Alternative kill mechanisms not shown in this diagram include chemical lasers and particle-beam weapons.

For some space defense applications, particle-beam weapons may eventually constitute a realistic alternative to the use of lasers in space. A particle-beam weapon hurls a stream of protons or ions toward its target. When the particles slam into the target, they disrupt the operation of its electronic devices or they bore into its surface to cause structural damage. Other promising damage mechanisms include the ignition of the gases and liquids carried in the tanks of the missile, or the destruction of the explosive charges used in triggering the detonation of its nuclear warheads.

The thought of forming a protective barrier around our country with a swarm of orbiting robots may seem a little far-fetched. But actually, for several years robots have been used in space to handle a variety of useful assignments including simulated military attacks. Specifically, in the past decade the Russians have tested at least a dozen killer satellites in space. Their assignments? To seek out targets previously launched by the Russians, sneak up on them, and blast them to smithereens with a weapon resembling a sawed-off shotgun.

Most spacefaring military robots, however, are much friendlier than that. For years America's reconnaissance satellites have been taking snapshots of strategic regions of the earth. When the satellite finishes taking a particular series of pictures, it automatically ejects a film packet, which releases a parachute on entering the atmosphere and is snatched from the air by a special military aircraft.

Other important precursors of the robot revolution in space have been soft-landed on the moon. America's *Surveyor* spacecraft, which dug a narrow slit trench in the lunar soil under the direction of technicians back on earth, is a good example. So are the two Lunohods, those compact Russian moon carts that wheeled around the lunar landscape in the 1970s making scientific measurements and snapping photographs for transmission back to Russian laboratories. The *Viking* spacecraft, which NASA's technicians sent to the surface of Mars in hopes of achieving new scientific insights and finding new life forms, was another impressive space-age robot. According to calculations put together by the well-known astrophysicist Dr. Carl Sagan, *Viking* was by one standard "about as smart as a grasshopper," but from a different point of view it was "only as intelligent as a bacterium." Dr. Sagan did not make these comparisons in a demeaning way; he greatly admires both aerospace engineering and the clever way Mother Nature has managed to build complicated creatures using only unskilled labor.

The *Viking* spacecraft had two "eyes," but they worked in the infrared, not the visible, portion of the electromagnetic spectrum. It was also equipped with a simple arm that could push rocks out of the way, dig holes, and pick up samples of the Martian soil under the watchful scrutiny of its designers back on earth. A separate little "finger" measured wind speed and direction. The *Viking* was also rigged to measure Mars quakes and to ferret out living microbes if any were hidden in shallow burrows under the surface of the planet. Nuclear isotopes supplied energy to the radio transmitters that relayed *Viking*'s findings back to scientists at the Jet Propulsion Laboratory.

On November 17, 1970, Soviet space scientists successfully launched an unmanned spacecraft onto a rendezvous trajectory with the moon. It carried on board the Lunohod, a remote-controlled wire-wheeled cart designed to explore the lunar landscape. For several weeks thereafter, Russian technicians "drove" their lunar robot around the boulders on the moon by remote teleoperator control. Although the experiment was a success, controlling the movements of the lunar buggy was considerably more difficult than they had expected. Signal travel times were a major problem. The Lunohod's television images required 1.5 seconds to travel to the earth; a similar amount of time was then required for the operator's control signals to get back to the moon.

When necessary, the JPL scientists sent back detailed instructions to control the spacecraft's behavior.

The large manipulator arm masterminded in Canada for use on the Shuttle orbiter provides another interesting example of teleoperation in space, although it is directed by the astronauts aboard the Shuttle rather than an operator located on the ground. The Canadian arm is 50 feet long, which probably makes it the largest remote manipulator ever constructed. It was designed for use in the weightlessness of space; on the ground it is not strong enough to support its own weight.

Because of the enormous success of robots and remote manipulators in space, some experts argue that almost any task we might want to perform there could best be handled without man's presence. This approach would produce definite economies. For one thing, the booster rockets needed to transport robots into orbit could be much smaller and lighter. Complicated life-support systems are also unnecessary, and there is little need for routine expendable supplies such as air, water, toothpaste, or shaving cream.

Moreover, the presence of astronauts in a space vehicle can cause serious problems for certain kinds of on-board machinery. When the astronauts move about, they tend to create small, random g loads, thus jiggling the equipment. A key reason for moving manufacturing processes into space is to take advantage of the low-disturbance environment usually found there. Unexpected vibrations tend to play havoc with space manufacturing procedures such as the making of optical glasses and vaccines in zero g. Certain pieces of equipment such as the space telescope are totally intolerant of the disturbances that would be created by human beings on board. Even shallow breathing by an astronaut would spoil any astronomical observations.

Recently, Grumman Aerospace proposed the development of a new free-flying robot for use in connection with the Space Shuttle. It would be especially useful for missions in which the Shuttle must rendezvous with a disabled satellite or one that requires fresh supplies of fuel. If necessary, the Shuttle could handle such a mission on its own without outside help. Unfortunately, its rendezvous rockets spew out a sooty gas which coats and contaminates delicate spacecraft components such as thermal sensors and solar cells. The engineers at Grumman have proposed the construction of a remote teleoperator called the POV—Proximity Operations Vehicle. It is specially designed to minimize spacecraft contamination. The POV is a 30-cubic-foot box with a gangling arm protruding from each of its four corners. Each of the arms carries four thrustors powered by noncontaminating nitrogen gas.

When the POV flies out to meet a satellite, the astronauts aboard the Shuttle will maneuver it by remote control. Their control panel provides them with a picture from either of the two television cameras carried aboard the craft—one pointing forward in the direction of travel of the POV, the other pointing aft. Once the Proximity Operations Vehicle reaches its destination, a grappling device will emerge from its front end, grab the disabled satellite, and take it in tow.

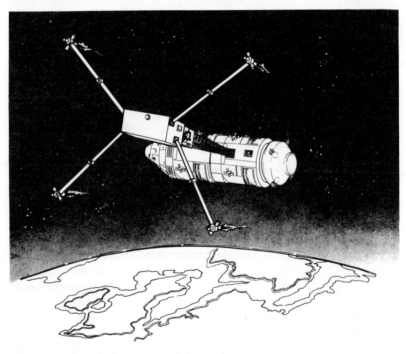

The Proximity Operations Vehicle (POV), a concept proposed by Grumman Aerospace, consists of a boxy remote manipulator operated by the astronauts in the Space Shuttle, who watch and respond to television pictures transmitted to them by cameras carried aboard the POV. Four long, spindly arms attached to the spacecraft are each tipped with four gaseous-nitrogen thrustors to control the flight path and orientation of the vehicle. When the POV reaches a disabled satellite, it takes it in tow with its grappling device for a quick trip back to the Shuttle orbiter.

Grumman's POV minimizes spacecraft contamination and saves fuel. Its gaseous-nitrogen propellant is not very efficient, but the vehicle itself is so light that moving it around in space is much easier than lugging around the massive Shuttle orbiter—even though the Shuttle's propulsion system uses much better propellants. Rudolf Adornato, Grumman's manager of satellite services, makes the following comparison: "The propellant used by the POV for a typical rendezvous mission would be less than 100 pounds. For the Shuttle it's more like 500 to 1,200 pounds." Adornato also believes that his company's creation will grow and evolve into a more capable spacefaring robot in the future: "Later versions, equippped with sets of grappling arms, could even repair satellites without bringing them back to the Shuttle." Similar teleoperators may someday be used in assembling large structures in space and in the maintenance and repair of satellites located in hard-to-reach orbits, including those at the geosynchronous altitude. Engineers at Rockwell International have proposed one version with three swiveling arms that will automatically match the rotational rate of tumbling spacecraft before latching on to it to take it in tow.

In many respects, future remote manipulators to be operated on the bottoms of the deepest oceans will resemble the robots already being operated or planned for use in outer space. Common assignments for "inner space" robots will include rescue and salvage operations and the recovery of minerals and hydrocarbons in large quantities.

Although they appear rather mundane, the manganese nodules scattered across vast regions of the ocean floor contain abundant concentrations of a number of important minerals. Single specimens weighing 500 pounds or more have been found in some locations; but a more normal sample measures less than 3 inches across. One observer has compared them to "little potatoes overcooked on a charcoal grill."

In the next few years, these "little potatoes" will likely become the basis of a major new industry. In some regions, principally in the Pacific Ocean between California and Hawaii, the nodules are so plentiful they resemble cobblestone pavements left behind by some extinct civilization. On the average they contain about 30 percent manganese, 1.25 percent nickel, 1 percent copper, and 0.25 percent cobalt. A ton of them is usually worth somewhere between $150 and $300, or roughly the same price pound for pound as raw petroleum.

In the 1970s, when the National Science Foundation studied the feasibility of seafloor mining, it placed the value of one 1.6-million-square-mile area in the North Pacific region at $10 million per square mile. Some industry spokesmen believe that the panel members were a bit optimistic; but even the lowest estimates are never below $2 million to $4 million per square mile. Even taking the most conservative figure, a single region of the ocean floor roughly one-fifth the size of the continental United States has mineral wealth valued at more than $3 trillion, or about one year's Gross National Product for our entire country.

Several large companies are trying to perfect submersible robots to locate and gather seafloor nodules. Here is a description of an early attempt to achieve large-scale retrieval:

> A cross-legged, gimballed derrick towered above the deck. Below the keel, 17,000 feet of pipe curved gently to the bottom of the Pacific Ocean. A vacuum chamber on the end of the pipe sucked up black lumps from the cold ooze like a voracious mechanical elephant picking its way through acres of spilled peanuts. A series of pumps on the pipe string moved the crushed lumps upward in a salt water slurry. At 6:26 A.M. on March 28, 1978, a stream of wet ore began to splash into the hold of the ship.

It was an exciting moment for the crew. This was the first successful attempt anywhere by anyone to produce a continuous stream of metal ore from the ocean floor.

In many areas the ocean floor is far too slippery to permit the efficient use of wheeled vehicles. Consequently, the robots being designed to pluck manganese nodules from the bottom of the sea are nearly always provided with other means of locomotion. The *Glomar Explorer*, for instance, uses a sledlike nodule plucker that propels itself forward with horizontally mounted spinning screws. Two long metal cylinders run along the sides of the crawler. A spiral blade resembling the thread of an Archimedes' screw curls gently around each cylinder. As the crawler slithers along the bottom, it rakes up any loose nodules that have been spotted by its video camera. When the nodules are collected, they are crushed and mixed with saltwater to make a slurry which can be pumped to the surface through an 18-inch pipe more than 3 miles long. The overall system includes a television camera, high-intensity lights, and a sonar unit used in positioning the crawler relative to a network of bottom-mounted sonar transducers. Hovering over the crawler, 100 feet above the bottom of the sea, is a boxlike

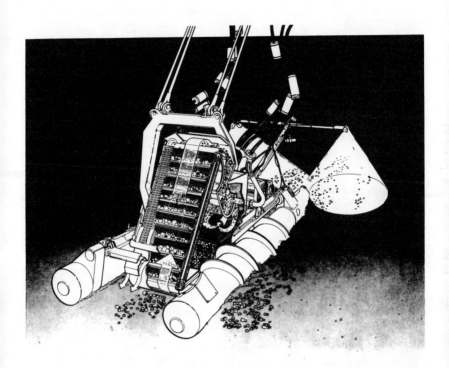

Economical exploitation of the manganese nodules littering the bottom of the sea will require large-scale continuous mining operations. This bottom crawler is being tested in the middle of the Pacific Ocean. The spiral metal blades on the sides of the crawler rotate to propel it forward on almost any type of surface, including slippery mud. The device shown in this drawing weighs 100 tons and is as big as a single-family house. Commercial versions will probably be at least three times as wide and about ten times as heavy. When the nodules have been scooped up by the crawler, they are crushed into a powder and mixed with seawater for pumping to the surface through a long metal pipe.

station used in pumping the slurry to the surface. The ship and the free-floating pumping station move along in tandem at a speed of about 1 knot.

Dr. Robert Ballard, a geologist at the Woods Hole Oceanographic Institution on Cape Cod, Massachusetts, has proposed the development of a different kind of remotely controlled robot for undersea research. His concept calls for the use of a freewheeling robot carrying another smaller robot just in case the parent craft spots something that warrants a more detailed examination. Dr. Ballard calls his robotic duo "Argo" and "Jason." Argo, with Jason firmly nestled inside, will be towed by a ship over the mid-oceanic ridge. The contours of this enormous undersea "mountain" range, which covers one-fourth of the entire globe, have been mapped by teams of researchers for more than a decade, but so far, scarcely 1 percent of the maps have been completed. "When Argo/Jason is in use, we will be able to explore hundreds of miles of the seafloor each month, rather than the few square miles now possible," notes Dr. Ballard.

Cruising in water as deep as 20,000 feet, Argo will carry imaging pods to scan the ridge from a safe range while serving as a temporary garage for Jason. If one of the Argo cameras spots a noteworthy feature, Jason will be deployed on a tether to investigate. The smaller Jason will be able to get much closer to the feature (an important consideration when the water is dark and murky), and he will be equipped with stereoscopic color-television eyes and manipulator arms for sample collection. Why did Dr. Ballard opt for the use of robots rather than a manned system? "Man's presence on the seafloor is not as an explorer," he explains. "He's on his hands and knees with a flashlight." Moreover, even in shallow water a diver can rarely stay on station for more than 6 hours; a deep dive that long requires hundreds of man-hours of careful preparations. Dr. Ballard's robotic duo is being designed to remain submerged for 30 days or more.

Most landlubber robots are stationary. Those that do move are usually mounted on wheels or tractor treads. However, Odetics, a small aerospace-equipment manufacturer in Anaheim, California, is developing a six-legged walking robot that skitters over rough terrain like a massive metal beetle. The "Functionoid," as its creators call it, can also perform several other stunts. In March of 1983, in a demonstration for the media, it lifted the rear end of a small pickup truck and walked across the room with it. Then, by gingerly lifting its six

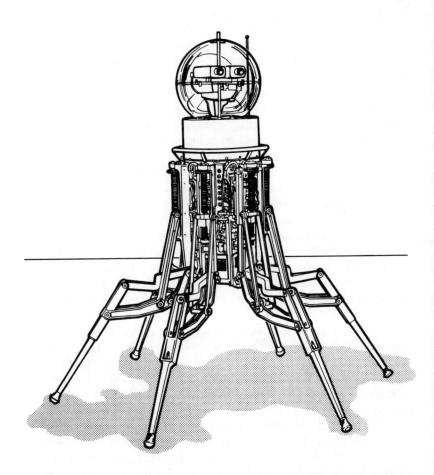

Like an ungainly insect out for an early-morning stroll, the six-legged "Functionoid" robot designed and built by the Odetics Corporation skitters over rough terrain under precise microprocessor control. Hot off the assembly line, the Functionoid stands more than 6 feet tall, weighs 370 pounds, and has demonstrated the capability of lifting a 3,000-pound load.

legs one at a time in just the right sequence, the Functionoid climbed into the bed of the truck. Functionoid weighs only 370 pounds, but it can lift a 3,000-pound load. It can also climb irregular surfaces and execute such difficult motions as walking and rotating at the same time. Ten on-board computers control the robot's complex movements. After seeing the public demonstration, several robotics experts concluded that the ungainly device significantly pushes forward several important technologies.

Odetics Chairman Joel Slutzky believes that his company's robot could be built in mass-production quantities for about $200,000 a copy. Promising commercial markets include dangerous mining jobs, handling of toxic wastes, and the cleanup of radioactive spills. Military uses may include reconnaissance, the clearing of hazardous minefields, and chemical warfare.

Many of the same clever technologies that are permitting modern robots to venture into such hostile environments as minefields, outer space, and the bottom of the ocean are being used in the creation of a new breed of manipulators intended to help a group of individuals who must spend their lives in extraordinarily difficult circumstances: the physically handicapped. One of these technologies uses the incapacitated body of the paraplegic as a sort of ready-made "robot." The first widely publicized demonstration of this new approach took place in 1982 in Dayton, Ohio, when Nan Davis, a 22-year-old paraplegic senior at Wright State University, stood in front of network television crews and took a half-dozen jerky strides.

Nan's halting movements were triggered and controlled by electrical impulses flowing from a microcomputer through a mass of multicolored wires to thirty electrodes taped over the major muscles of her incapacitated legs. The microcomputer, using a program developed by Dr. Jerrold Petrofsky, who masterminded and supervised the overall project, figured out the exact time to send each impulse into her leg muscles. Sensors monitored the movements and responses of her ankles, knees, and hips. This information was fed back into the computer. Miss Davis was elated by her experience, but a little self-conscious at the frantic media attention she received. As she took her first stride since her accident, the room echoed with tender applause. "One step for mankind," she said with a nervous grin.

"The device is a mass of wires right now," admitted one of the technicians working on the project, "but it will eventually be a small microprocessor capable of being implanted pacemaker style." About 30 percent of Nan's weight was supported by a parachute harness, and during the demonstration she used her hands to grip a set of parallel bars running the length of the 10-foot walkway.

Dr. Petrofsky believes that with a little luck, his system could be ready for commercialization sometime during the next decade. According to some of his colleagues, it could take longer; but in any case, the methods he and his team have pioneered are already helping many who have lost the use of their legs. His computer program allows paraplegics to "ride" a stationary bicycle, thus keeping their paralyzed limbs from atrophying, the usual outcome following paralysis. Many of the handicapped who are participating in his program have amazingly muscular legs. Weak electrical shocks cause their muscles to twitch and move, thus helping them maintain proper muscle tone. Some athletes who have broken their legs are using the same method to stay in shape during their recuperation. One dedicated individual had to have his cast changed in mid-treatment—his legs had become so muscular that the cast was uncomfortably tight! In the past when casts were changed because of discomfort, it was usually caused by muscle shrinkage.

In the long run, the teleoperator technologies being pioneered by Dr. Jerrold Petrofsky and his colleagues at other research centers will likely result in some novel and interesting approaches to athletic training for specialist and nonspecialist alike. For instance, within a few years you may be able to enroll in a special program designed to help you learn to execute a perfect tennis stroke. Your instructor will be a robot, and you will *wear* him when you are under instruction.

Immediately after you arrive at the training center dressed in your tennis outfit, a computer will scan your body with its electronic eyes to measure the lengths of the various segments of your arms and legs so that you can be fitted into a robotlike device resembling a whole-body prosthesis. Every mechanical linkage of the robot will be tailored for a snug fit, thus making him remarkably comfortable to wear. Once you are wearing your robot instructor, he will become an amazingly efficient tutor urging you, with supreme patience, toward perfection in the game. As the ball crosses the net, his robot eyes will analyze its trajectory and your body position to determine exactly how you should hit it. Your robot will, incidentally, make helpful comments on your game using his voice-synthesizer chip, and will understand your replies, although he may have problems knowing how to react to emotional outbursts.

Once you are on the tennis court, your robot instructor will show you how to execute the various standard backhand and forehand strokes over and over again, gradually correcting any flaws in your form. For instance, if you tend to face the net too much, he will gently but firmly turn your feet toward the sidelines. If you are hitting the ball too late, he will make adjustments in your form a little at a time so that you will soon be hitting it at the proper location in front of your body. Of course, the robot will always confide in you vocally whenever he makes any important changes in your game. Every shot

Someday you may be able to "wear" a special robot tennis instructor who will teach you how to execute perfect strokes. The linkages in the instructional robot will be adjustable to provide an extremely comfortable fit. Once you are wearing your tennis instructor, he will patiently lead you through the most efficient possible strokes by means of subtle body pressures and spoken comments. Similar devices will be available to teach golf, billiards, racquetball, and a number of other competitive sports.

he teaches you will be optimized by his computer for your own particular body size and shape. Moreover, he will be able to repeat the same perfect strokes over and over for you until the "feel" of them is forever burned into your brain.

The robot tennis instructor will have a number of interesting characteristics. For one thing, he will allow you to hit the ball (taking into account differences in physiology) the same way your favorite player does. Simply tell him whom you admire and which shot you want to execute, and the robot will search his electronic memory for the desired characteristics. He will then play the stroke through your body as many times as you like in rapid succession. In a single half-hour session you will be able to hit Roscoe Tanner's cannonball serve, Rod Laver's topspin backhand, and just for good measure, the famous two-handed backhand of Chris Evert Lloyd. Incidentally, if your favorite player is left-handed and you hit right-handed, or if he is male and you are female or vice versa, it will not make any difference to the robot: his computer will automatically make the necessary adjustments.

If robotic sports training turns out to be popular and profitable, it could result in new types of sports events in which the competitors would be allowed to wear their robots in tournament play. Would Tracy Austin wearing a Pancho Gonzales robot be able to stay on the court with Jimmy Connors who is wearing the robot of Evonne Goolagong? One problem is sure to arise: the television commentators will become utterly confused, especially if the match is mixed doubles.

Science writer David Yates has a different idea for the recreational use of space-age robots. He believes that within a few years the technology may be good enough to allow you to go on special vacation "trips" and do the standard things tourists enjoy (like riding the elevators to the top of the Eiffel Tower or wandering through the Sistine Chapel) without ever leaving your favorite armchair. Suppose you live in Buffalo but you would like to spend a lazy Sunday afternoon poking around among the ancient ruins of Pompeii. You would begin your "vacation trip" by picking up the telephone and calling a proxy-robot service. Once you have the proper travel agent on the line, you can rent a robot for an hour, a day, a week—whatever you may prefer. Sitting at your control panel in your living room, you will begin operating your own personal robot in Naples (the closest city to Pompeii with proxy robots for rent). Let's allow David Yates himself to pick up the commentary for the next part of our story:

Soon you are in control of a proxy, moving cautiously out of its resting "garage" to mingle with the human crowds on the streets of Naples. Pompeii is a bus journey away, but this is no problem, because the proxy has a credit card. . . . You enjoy the visit, chat with the guide and take some photographs with the camera thoughtfully provided by the hire service. . . . You buy some souvenirs which you take to a packing and posting service.

Your robot vacation trip to the ruins of Pompeii turns out to be much like the millions of European trips taken by American tourists each year. Of course, there are a few minor differences. For one thing, you will not be able to sample the native foods and the local wines. On the other hand, there are small compensations: you will escape the ravages of Montezuma's Revenge no matter where you may decide to go. Muggings, mosquito bites, and fatal accidents will also be a very unlikely part of your "armchair" vacation. This certain safety is comforting, but it will also take some of the adventure out of your trip. Fortunately, some novel and adventuresome robot vacations will also be available. Would you enjoy a relaxing climb to the top of the Matterhorn? How about a Sunday picnic on a glacier in Antarctica? Or a leisurely afternoon rummaging in the sunken wreckage of the British liner *Titanic*? Still not satisfied? David Yates proposes a smaller-model proxy robot that would allow you to study the beauties of the Amazon rain forest from a unique vantage point— as seen through the eyes of a flying squirrel!

For many years M.I.T. Professor Dr. Marvin Minsky, one of the pioneers in artificial intelligence, has been working on his ideas for much broader and more profitable applications of space-age robotics. His concept is similar to but more elaborate than the ideas advanced by David Yates. Dr. Minsky calls his scheme "telepresence." Specifically, he would like to see the large-scale use of robots and teleoperators as the only workers in dangerous oil fields and coal mines. An accident or a cave-in might destroy a crew of robots and cost a few million dollars. But it would almost never cost human lives. Nor would it lead to Congressional investigations or make the headlines, except, perhaps, in industry trade papers.

Dr. Minsky also wants to use advanced teleoperator technology to shrink or magnify the forces and the movements of the human fingers. For instance, a surgeon might perform delicate microsurgery by using his own hands to control the movements of a much smaller robot, perhaps even one of microscopic size. A computer could easily scale the movements appropriately. With proper feedback from subminiaturized sensors, the surgeon should be able to "feel" the textures of various tissues and organs so that he could operate successfully on damaged nerves, clogged arteries, or detached retinas without invading the body, except to make a small slit to insert his tiny manually controlled robot. Surgery of this type would be much safer and less painful than the conventional kind. In fact, so little extraneous tissue would be damaged that the patient might be able to return to his home the same day.

In Chapter 3 when we gazed backward through time, we encountered some rather outlandish descriptions of early robots lurking in the shadows of history: "gold and silver trees decorated with mechanical birds that sang and raised their wings" and "stray houseflies driven away by a bronze fly." Of course, we understood, almost immediately, that these were mythological accounts.

But what if we could turn the situation around? What if we could somehow expose the individuals who concocted these fanciful tales to the material contained in the pages of this book? Would they accept what we have related as fact? Or fiction? Would they actually believe that their descendants have learned to build such marvelous devices from common, everyday materials? Or would they assume that we had developed some wonderfully imaginative legends and fairy tales?

Specifically, would they be convinced that we in the future could fill the sky with swift chariots able to vaporize our enemies with thin beams of light? Would they believe that we had constructed a cabinet capable of playing chess on its own—unaided by human beings—but aided by advice from a similar cabinet thousands of miles away? Would they accept our story about a workshop in a distant land where all the human laborers journey home at night, only to have their work continue uninterrupted? (Doesn't that sound more like a story from The Arabian Nights than an accurate, scientific description?)

And yet no matter how strange and outlandish our descriptions might seem to be, they are merely the factual characteristics of planned or existing robots. Arthur C. Clarke has observed that to the uninitiated, advanced technology is "indistinguishable from magic." In the case of the technology associated with robotics, he is most assuredly correct. Still, by all accounts, we have barely begun to exploit the potentialities of the robot revolution. When the self-replicating robots now being born at the foot of Mount Fuji become widely affordable, there will be no apparent limit to the technological wonders we can foresee.

HOBBY ROBOTICS MATERIALS

This appendix contains information of special interest to those who would like to build their own hobby or promotional robots. It includes a list of magazines and periodicals devoted to the needs of the hobbyists, the names and addresses of hobby-related organizations, and a listing of companies that supply fully assembled hobby robots or the components used in their construction.

The table in this Appendix lists journals and periodicals that contain regular articles dealing with issues and technologies of interest to those in the robotics industry or those who would like to prepare for participation in the industry.

The following organizations and clubs help promote robotics and provide opportunities for social events involving individuals with an interest in industrial or hobby robotics:

1. *Robotics Experimenters Amateur League (REAL)*

   International Robotics Foundation
   P.O. Box 3227
   Seal Beach, CA 90740
   Thomas Carroll (213) 596–9769
   John Gutman (404) 972–7082

2. *International Institute for Robotics*

>   P.O. Box 210708
>   Dallas, TX 75211

3. *Robotics International of SME*

>   One SME Drive
>   P.O. Box 930
>   Dearborn, MI 48128
>   Phone (313) 271–1500

4. *Robot Institute of America*

>   P.O. Box 930
>   Dearborn, MI 48128
>   Phone (313) 271–0778

The following companies supply experimental or hobby robots or the components used in their manufacture:

1. *Android Amusement (213) 303–2434*

>   1408 East Arrow Highway
>   Irwindale, CA 91706

2. *Universal Robot Systems (213) 596–9769*

>   7025 El Paseo Street
>   Long Beach, CA 90815

3. *The Robot Factory (303) 687–6208*

>   P.O. Box 112
>   Cascade, CO 80809

4. *Rebs Robots (713) 621–8429*

>   3530 Timmons Lane, #155
>   Houston, TX 77027

5. *Hobby Robot Company (912) 375–7821*

>   P.O. Box 997
>   Lilburn, GA 30247

6. *Heath Company (616) 982–3309*

>   Hilltop Road
>   St. Joseph, MI 49085

7. *Rhino Robots* *(217) 352–8485*

   308 South State Street
   Champaign, IL 61820

8. *General Development Company* *(602) 866–1672*

   312 East Breaburn Street
   Phoenix, AZ 85022

9. *Microbot, Inc.* *(800) 227–8909*

   453-H Ravendale Drive
   Mountain View, CA 94043

10. *Robot Repair* *(916) 441–1166*

    816½ 21st Street
    Sacramento, CA 95814

11. *RB Robot Corporation* *(303) 279–5525*

    14618 West Sixth Avenue
    Golden, CO 80401

12. *Isaac Robotics* *(518) 471–6763*

    P.O. Box 138
    Old Chatham, NY 12136

13. *World of Robots* *(800) 248–0896*

    2335 East High Street
    Jackson, MI 49203

ROBOTICS JOURNALS AND PERIODICALS

PERIODICAL	ADDRESS	COMMENTS
Robotics Age	Strand Bldg. 174 Concord Street Peterborough, NH 03458	An excellent experimenter's magazine. Bimonthly.
Robotics Today	Robotics International of SME One SME Drive Box 930 Dearborn, MI 48128	Emphasizes industrial robotics. Bimonthly.
The International Journal of Robotics Research	The MIT Press 28 Carleton Street Cambridge, MA 02142	A quarterly, scholarly journal. Highly technical.
The Industrial Robot	IFS Publishing Company Kempston Redford MK 42 7BT ENGLAND	Expensive, technical.
Robot Builder	International Robotics Foundation/Robot Experimenters Amateur League P.O. Box 3227 Seal Beach, CA 90740	A newsletter, experimenter-oriented. Published irregularly.
Hobby Robot Design Notes	Hobby Robot Company P.O. Box 997 Lilburn, GA 30247	Experimental robotics. Quarterly publication.
BYTE	McGraw-Hill 70 Main Street Peterborough, NH 03458	A monthly personal-computer magazine with occasional robotics coverage.
Interface Age	16704 Marquardt Avenue Cerritos, CA 90701	Personal-computer coverage. April issues deal with hobby robotics.

SUGGESTED READING

1. Friedrich, Otto; Redman, Christopher; and Simpson, Janice C. "The Robot Revolution." *Time*, December 8, 1980. pp. 72–83.
2. Cohen, John. *Human Robots in Myth and Science*. A. S. Barnes. Cranbury, N.J. 1967.
3. Logsdon, Tom. *Computers and Social Controversy*. Computer Science Press. Rockville, Maryland. 1980.
4. Dreyfus, Hubert L., *What Computers Can't Do*. Harper and Row. New York, N.Y. 1972.
5. McCorduck, Pamela. *Machines Who Think*. W. H. Freeman. San Francisco. 1979.
6. Logsdon, Tom. *How to Cope with Computers*. Hayden. Rochelle Park, N.J. 1982.
7. Weitzenbaum, Joseph. *Computer Power and Human Reason*. W. H. Freeman. San Francisco, Calif. 1979.
8. Albus, James. *Brains, Behavior, and Robotics*. Byte Books. Peterborough, New Hampshire. 1981.
9. Loofburrow, Todd. *How to Build a Computer-Controlled Robot*. Hayden Book Co., Rochelle Park, N.J. 1978

195

10. Engleberger, Joseph. *Robotics in Practice*. American Management Assoc. (AMA-COM), New York, N.Y. 1980.
11. D'Ignazio, Fred. *Working Robots*. Elsevier/Nelson Books. New York, N.Y. 1982.
12. Krasnoff, Barbara. *Robots: Reel to Real*. Arco Publishing Co., New York, N.Y. 1982.

INDEX

ACRONYM vision system, 67
Adornato, Rudolf, 179
Afghanistan, Soviet vehicles in, 127
Aiken, Howard H., 48
AIM-65 computer, 165
aircraft, 14
  assembling of, 69, 97–98
  obsolete, 127
  RPV's and, 116, 123–27
  testing of, 126
Air Force, U.S., 107, 126
  Wasp program of, 122–23
Albus, James, 29–30
amusement parks, robots in, 45,
  147–48
Analytical Engine, 48, 84, 108
Android Amusement Corporation,
  138–40, 164, 192
Android Design (Weinstein), 162

androids, 39–40, 45, 59
  robots vs., 18
Antium, robotlike creatures in, 34
Apollo 13 astronauts, rescue of, 62–
  63
Applicon Corporation, 106
Arab-Israeli war (1967), 117, 118
arc welding, robots used for, 22
Argentina, in Falkland Islands war,
  113–14, 115, 116–17
Argo (ocean robot), 182
Argon series robots, 138
Aristotle, 34
Armatron robot, 154
arms, robot, 22–25, 146, 157
  of hobby robots, 165–66
  human arms compared to, 22
  pairs of, 14, 22
  single, 22

Army, U.S., 129
artificial intelligence, 55, 78–96,
    151–52
    applications of, 79–80, 82–92,
        94–96
    definition of, 79
    early research on, 83
    human intelligence compared to,
        52, 79, 82–83, 91
    limits of, 54, 80–83, 91
    testing of, 92–94, 96
Asimov, Isaac, 45–46, 142
Aspin, Lee, 170
asps, mechanical, 39
assembly lines, robot, 11–14, 16,
    25, 54, 62
    Exocet missile compared to, 114
    in factories of future, 97–100
    safety, precautions on, 12, 21
athletic training, 185–87
Australia, robotics research in, 14–
    15
auto industry:
    CAD/CAM and, 105
    robot industry compared to, 29
    robots used in, 12–13, 22, 27–
        28, 54
    in U.S. vs. Japan, 28
Aztecs, mechanical devices of, 34

Babbage, Charles, 48, 84, 108
backgammon-playing computers,
    87–88
Bagley T. Brat (robot), 141
Ballard, Robert, 182
Barnett, Joseph, 134
Basile, Giambattista, 43
batch-processing facilities, efficiency
    of, 106–7, 111
Beley, Gene, 138–40
Bell & Howell, 110, 111
Belle (chess-playing computer), 86
Bell Telephone Laboratories, 49
Berliner, Hans, 87–88
binary number system, 64–65
binocular vision, 25, 65–67
"bin stacking" problem, 63
biological robots, 41–44

birds, mechanical, 34
Blank, Ted, 167
blind robots, 12, 14, 25, 58
Blitzkrieg tactics, 118
blood infections, diagnosis of, 89, 91
Boddy, Jack, 100–102
bomb scares, 140
Bonaparte, Napoleon, 35
Bonham, Douglas, 156
Bonzo, Hector, 117
"boomerang" system, 131–32
Bradbury, Ray, 41
"brains," 16, 54–55, 58, 59, 114
    of Electro, 134
    electronic, 15, 46–49
    of hobby robots, 162
    microprocessors as, 19, 20, 145–
        146
    of Mobot I, 49
    processing capacity of, 63
    of robot tanks, 130
Brewster, Sir David, 38
Brown, John Seeley, 91
Buck Rogers in the 25th Century
    (movie), 137
Build Your Own Working Robot
    (Heiserman), 157
Business Week magazine, 27
Buster (hobby robot), 157–59
Bylinsky, Gene, 105, 107

CAD (computer-aided design), 100–
    106
    definition of, 100
    early programs in, 103–4
    effectiveness of, 102–3
    methods for forming pictures in,
        102
    Space Shuttle and, 101–2
CAD/CAM, 106–12
    growth of, 111
    power and promise of, 104–6
    purpose of, 108
CADUCEUS (expert system), 89, 90
California:
    military robots in, 127–29
    robot carts in, 109–11
    robot industry in, 23–25, 58–59,

138–40, 182–84
Calvino, Italo, 41
CAM (computer-aided
    manufacturing), 104–12
  definition of, 100
  see also CAD/CAM
cameras:
  Scout, 123–24
  video, 165, 180
Canada, 125, 177
cancer, treatment of, 89, 90
Čapek, Karel, 18, 44
Carnegie-Mellon Robotics Center,
    58, 68, 87
Carroll, Sue, 142–44
Carroll, Thomas, 142–45, 146,
    164, 167
cartlike robots, 22, 100, 109–11
Cenowa, Ronald A., 105
centrifugal governors, 60–62
Charles Augustus, Duke of Saxe-
    Weimar, 38
Charlie (robot), 146–47
Checkers, 36
  game tree for, 84–85, 86
chemical lasers, 173, 174
chess, 35–36, 85–87
  game tree for, 85–86
children's toys, 41
  motor in, 152, 153
chocolate snatching, 14, 22
Christie, Julie, 33
Chrysler, 12
Cincinnati Malicron, 27
Clarke, Arthur C., 189
clockwork mechanisms, 36, 37, 40
Clyde the Claw (robot), 28
coal miners, decline in number of,
    32
Cohen, John, 38
Coleman, David, 140–41
color-recognition capability, 134,
    136
Colossus series robots, 142, 144, 164
Commander Robot I, 140–41
computer-aided design, see CAD
computer-aided manufacturing, see
    CAM

computer industry, growth of, 29
Computer Power and Human
    Reason (Weitzenbaum), 81,
    82–83
computer programs, 20, 62, 82–88
  ELIZA, 82–83
  game-playing, 83–88
computers:
  binary numeration system of, 64–
    65
  brain compared to, 83
  cartoon versions of, 45
  ENIAC, 46–49
  in feedback control, 60–62
  hierarchy of, 108–9
  military robots guided by, 114,
    116, 117, 118, 120, 124
  real-time processing of, 62–63
  robots as muscles of, 15–16, 19,
    20
  size of, 137
  user-friendly, 80, 83, 88, 95
  vision analysis and, 68–69
  see also artificial intelligence
Congress, U.S., 31, 102
Conqueror (British submarine), 116
Consolidated Diesel Corporation
    (Condec), 51
conveyor belts, 109
Creative Engineering, 149
crimes, robots and, 140, 141, 145
criminal justice, computers and, 83
CRT (cathode-ray tube), 100, 102
  methods for forming pictures on,
    102, 103
cruise missiles, 119–23
  destabilizing effects of, 120
  low-altitude trajectory of, 119–20,
    121
  in World War II, 119–20
C3PO ("Star Wars" robot), 46, 47
culture, education and, 81
cup counting, 69, 70–72
cursive scanning, 102, 103
Czirr, J. Bart, 131–32

Darrach, Bradford, 52
data-storage-and-manipulation

problem, 62–65
Davis, Nan, 184–85
Defense Department, U.S., 51
Defense Mapping Agency, 122
delay timers, 154
delivery robots, 22
Delphi, Temple of, 34
Demon Seed (movie), 33
Dern, Bruce, 46
Devol, George C., 16, 50–51, 54,
    57
Digital Equipment Corporation, 68
diode inspectors, robots as, 14
dishpan robots, 152–54
Disney, Walt, 148
Disneyland, 45, 147
"Domestic Robot System," 154
Dreyfus, Hubert, 81
Drink Caddy robots (DC), 138–40,
    164

E&L Instruments, 157
Edison, Thomas, 31
education, changing views on, 81
Egypt, ancient, toys in, 41
Egypt, in Arab-Israeli conflict, 117,
    118
Eleazar of Worms, 41
electric current, alternating, Edison's
    opposition to, 31
Electro (robot), 134–37
electronic robots, 102
electronics industry, in Silicon
    Valley, 58
ELIZA computer program, 82–83
energy consumption, as measure of
    mechanical efficiency, 30
Engelberger, Joseph, 14, 51, 142
England:
    expert systems in, 90
    in Falkland Islands war, 113–14,
        115, 116–17
    industrial robots in, 14
ENIAC (Electronic Numerical
    Integrator and Calculator), 46–
    49
    precursors of, 48
Epcot Center, 147–48

Everest & Jennings, 164
Exocet missiles, 113–14, 115, 116
    cost of, 117
    guidance of, 114, 115
expert systems, 83, 88–92
    breakdown of, 91
    deep knowledge, 91–92
    fuzzy thinking in, 90–91
    problems with development of, 90
eyes, television, 56, 62–65, 69
    complications of, 62–63
    linear scanning as alternative to,
        65–66
    of Mobot I, 49, 50
    shades of gray distinguished by,
        63–65
    of Shakey, 51, 53

factory of the future, 97–112
    as computer-controlled robot, 100
    hierarchy of computers in, 108–9
    see also CAD; CAD/CAM; CAM
fake machines, 35–36
Falkland Islands war, 113–14, 115,
    116–17, 119
farm labor, decline of, 30, 32, 59
Federal Bureau of Investigation
    (FBI), 58
feedback control, 53, 60–62, 106,
    111, 172
Fifth Generation Computer, 94–95
Florida:
    robot-aided police in, 140
    robot industry in, 149
"flying eye" concept, 106
Forbidden Planet (movie), 46
Forbin Project, The (movie), 44–45
Fortune magazine, 111
France, artificial skin in, 75
Frederick the Great, 35
Functionoid robot, 169, 182–84
Futaba, 164

game-playing computers, 36, 83–88
Games People Play, 138
Gammonoid robot, 87–88
Garcan (armless robot), 159–60
Garvey, Charles J., 129–31

Gaylor, Noel, 127
General Belgrano, sinking of, 116–117
General Dynamics, 14, 123
General Electric, 27, 99
  CAD/CAM development at, 111–112
General Motors, 54, 147
  Fisher Body Division of, 105
George III, King of England, 35, 40
Glomar Explorer, 180–82
Goethe, Johann Wolfgang von, 38
Golden, Frederic, 170–71
golem stories, 41–42
"Good News from the Vatican" (Silverberg), 46
graphite, in military aircraft, 97–98, 127
Grierson, Donald K., 111–12
Griffin, Merv, 141
Grumman Aerospace, 177–79
Gunn, Thomas G., 107
Gutman, John, 167
gyroscopes, military, cleaning of, 128

hands, robot, 22–26, 146
  human hand compared to, 23, 24, 25, 26
  pairs of, 22
  programming and, 20, 24
  single, 22
  substitutes for, 14, 22
Hanebaum, H. W. (Bill), 128
Harbour, James E., 28
hardware, cost of, 59
Harvard University, 48
heart defects, diagnosis of, 90
Heath Company, 154–56
Hefner, Hugh, 138–40
Heiserman, David, 157–59
Henri, the Draftsman, 40
Herbach & Rademan, 152, 153
Herbug (mechanical turtle), 152
Hero-I (Heath Educational Robot), 154–56
Herzog, Chaim, 118

Highly Maneuverable Aircraft Technology (HiMAT), 126–27
Hill, James, 146–47
Hillis, William Daniel, 74–76
Hill-Norton, Lord, 114
Hilton, John, 28
HiMAT (Highly Maneuverable Aircraft Technology), 126–27
Hirose, Shigeo, 15
Hi Spot (RPV), 125
Hitachi, 58
hobby robotics clubs, 167–68
hobby robots:
  body dimensions of, 160
  building your own, 16, 150–68
  cost of, 152, 153, 154–56, 160
  design philosophies for, 160
  design steps for, 160–67
  major components of, 163
  promotional robots as, 138–47, 159–60
  purchase of, 16, 152, 154–57, 160
  sources of materials for, 152, 159–60, 191–93
Hodgkin's disease, protocols for, 90
Hoffmann, E. T. A., 43–44
Hopkins Beast (robot), 52–54
hostage crisis, rescue attempt in, 127
Hughes Aircraft, 49–50
Hughes Missile Systems Group, 123
human body, as kind of robot, 169, 184–87
Human Uses of Human Beings, The (Wiener), 31
hydraulic power, 22–23
hydraulic system, DC-10, CAD/CAM techniques and, 104–5

I, Robot (Asimov), 45
IBM, 27, 58, 91
ice-skating robots, 141
ILC-Dover, 125
Illiac IV computer, 95
Illinois:
  CAD/CAM in, 106
  industrial robots in, 27–28

Illinois, University of, 95
Indian legends, robotlike creatures in, 34
industrial robots, 11–14, 47, 107
    definitions and uses of, 16, 18–32
    efficiency of, 12–15, 28–30, 54
    future of, 16, 97–112
    intelligence of, 78–80, 94–96
    military functions of, 97–98, 127
    sensory capacities of, 54–77
    Sky Eye compared to, 125
    see also assembly lines, robot
industries, continuous-processing vs. batch-processing, 106, 111
infections, diagnosis of, 89, 91
insects, mechanical, 34
intercontinental ballistic robots, 116, 132
International Harvester, 105–6
International Institute of Robotics, 167, 192
International Robotics Foundation (IRF), 167, 191
Iran, hostage crisis in, 127
IRF (International Robotics Foundation), 167, 191
IRF/REAL (International Robotics Foundation/Robotics Experimenters' Amateur League), 146
Isaac (robot), 142
Israel:
    Lebanon invaded by (1982), 123
    in 1967 war, 117, 118
    RPV's of, 123–25

Jacquard, Joseph, 108
Jacquet-Droz, Pierre, 39–40
Japan:
    artificial intelligence in, 94–96
    Engleberger in, 51
    factory of the future in, 98–100
    hobby robots in, 154
    industrial robots in, 11–12, 14, 15, 21, 26, 27, 28, 29, 70
    robotics research in, 15
    robots as heroes in, 15, 27
    Soviet imports from, 127

U.S. competition with, 26, 28, 58, 94, 95–96
Jason (ocean robot), 182
Jefferson plant (Chrysler), 12
Jet Propulsion Laboratory (JPL), 25, 26, 176–77
job losses, from automation, 28, 31–32, 59
Johns Hopkins University, 52, 145

Kahn, Herman, 31
Kanade, Takeo, 68
Kawasaki plant, death at, 21, 70
Kennedy, John F., 31
Kentucky, futuristic factories in, 99
kill rates, of weapons, 119
Kinnucan, Paul, 67
Klatu Sales Promotional Robot, 138

Larkin, David, 111
laser battle stations, 170–75
Leach, Jim, 170
Lebanon:
    Israeli invasion of (1982), 123
    Palestinian massacre in (1982), 81–82
license-plate test, 94
Life magazine, 52
linear scanning, 65, 66
literature, robotlike creatures in, 18, 33, 41, 43–44, 45–46
"Little Lost Robot" (Asimov), 45
Lockheed Aircraft, 125
Lockheed-California, vision-guided robots of, 69
Lockwood, Gary, 33
Loew, Judah, 41–42
Loofburrow, Todd, 146, 164
Los Angeles Times, 140
Lovelace, Ada, 84, 108
Lowrey, Michael R., 68–69
Luddites, 31
Lunohods, 175, 176

Mabuchi RS-85 motor, 164
McCarthy, John, 78–79
McCormick, Bruce H., 95
McDonnell-Douglas, 14, 98

Machine Intelligence, 57–58, 63, 64
mail-delivery robots, 109–11
  nicknames of, 111
Mailmobile, 110
maintenance robots, 79
man-machine interfaces, 88
maps, digitized, 120, 122
Marianne, the Musician (robot), 40
Mark I computer, 48
Maverick air-to-surface antitank missiles, 119
medical diagnosis, 15, 80
  expert systems and, 89, 90
Merv Griffin television show, 141
Michigan:
  CAD/CAM in, 105
  industrial robots in, 12, 29
Microbot Corporation, 23, 154, 157
Micro Professor, 165
Mike (robot), 164
Milgram, David, 56–57, 63
Military Electronics magazine, 129–131
military robots, 16, 17, 79–80, 113–32
  accuracy of, 114, 116, 120, 122
  "boomerang" system, 131–32
  in Falkland Islands war, 113–14, 115, 116–17, 119
  in Middle East, 117, 118, 119
  Mr. Superclean, 127–29
  tanks, 116, 127, 129–31
  Wasp, 122–23
  see also cruise missiles; RPV's
Miller, Allan, 68–69
mineral deposits:
  location of, 91
  seafloor mining of, 179–82
Minimover 5 (experimental robot), 157
Minsky, Marvin, 79, 80, 188–89
Missouri, industrial robots in, 14
M.I.T., 81–83, 145
  Artificial Intelligence Laboratory at, 70–76
Mitsubishi, 154, 157, 158
Mobot I, 49–50

Moravec, Hans, 63
Moto-oka, Tohru, 94
Motorola 68000, 165
Move Master (hobby robot), 157, 158, 159
movement, 51–52, 145–46, 156
  of audioanimatronic characters, 147–48
  crane-like, 22
  of Electro, 134, 136
  of Gammonoid, 87–88
  of humans vs. robots, 22, 25
  of Mr. Superclean, 128–29
  of PUMA, 13
  of Teachmover, 23–25
movies, robotlike creatures in, 33, 44–45, 46, 59, 137, 138, 145
"Mr. Sandman" (song), 43
Mr. Superclean (robot), 127–29
multi-axis force-sensor system, 70–72
MYCIN (expert system), 89, 91
Myers, Jack, 89
myths and legends, robots in, 16, 34, 41

NASA, 95, 102, 126, 172, 175
National Science Foundation, 179–180
Naval Ocean Systems Center, 109–111
Neiman-Marcus, 154
New Zealand, 15
North Carolina, sighted robots in, 69
Northrop Aircraft, 97–98, 127
nuclear industry, programmed machine tools in, 108
nuclear-pumped X-ray lasers, 173
nuclear radiation, robots responsive to, 25
Nuclear Research Facility (Hanford, Wash.), 50
nuclear war:
  deterrent against, 131–32
  space-based defense against, 169–175

number system, binary vs. decimal,
64–65

ocean robots, 169, 179–82
Octek, gray-scale processing used by,
69
Odetics, 169, 182–84
Offenbach, Jacques, 44
Ohio:
futuristic factories in, 99
robot industry in, 27
Oldfield, Gene, 166
ONCASYN (expert system), 90

Palmer, E. Paul, 131–32
papermaking industry, 106, 111
parallel processing, 95
paraplegics, as robots, 184–85
Paris Air Show (1979), 123
particle-beam weapons, 174, 175
pattern recognition, 88, 145, 151–
152
Pennsylvania, futuristic factories in,
99
Pentamerone (Basile), 43
Persia, ancient, mechanical devices
in, 34, 41
Petrofsky, Jerrold, 184–85
petroleum refining, 106, 111
pixels (picture elements), 63–65
Pizza Time Theater, 148, 149
Plato, 34
play, functions of, 41
pneumatic power, 22–23
Poe, Edgar Allan, 35, 36
poker programs, 87
Polaroid, 165
population, human vs. robot, 12
positional notation system, 64–65
POV (Proximity Operations
Vehicle), 177–79
programmable machines, early
examples of, 40, 50
programming, 20–21, 151–52, 156,
166
methods of, 20, 24, 26

see also computer programs
promotional robots, 16, 133–37,
159–60
control systems of, 137
experts' objections to, 141
research contribution of, 141–42
of Westinghouse, 134–37
Prospector program, 91
Proteus IV, 33
Proximity Operations Vehicle
(POV), 177–79
psychotherapy, computer programs
and, 82–83
PUMA robots, 13, 23
punched holes, manufacturing
process controlled by, 107–8
Purbrick, John, 30–31, 70–74
Pygmalion, King of Cyprus, 34

Quasar Industries, 138

radar homing devices, 119, 120, 122
Radio Electronics, 157
Rand Corporation, 104
range-finding vision system, 67
Raphael, Bertram, 54
raster scanning, 102, 103
Raymond, Ray, 138
Reagan, Ronald, 169–71
REAL (Robot Experimenters
Amateur League), 167–68, 191
real-time processing, 62–63
Rebman, Jerry, 159–60
reconnaissance, 131
RPV's and, 123–25
Reichett, Tony, 138
remotely piloted vehicles, *see* RPV's
remote manipulators, *see*
teleoperators
restaurants, robots in, 137, 148–49
Rest of the Robots, The (Asimov), 45
Rhodes, G. W. (Dusty), 23, 25
Richardson, James J., 129–31
"Robot and the Bird, The" (show),
147

robot businesses, three kinds of, 16
Robot Experimenters Amateur
    League (REAL), 167–68, 191
Robot Factory, The, 140–41
Robotics Age, 167
robot industry, 51
    auto industry vs., 29
    profits in, 51, 54, 69
    small companies vs.
        conglomerates in, 27
    in U.S. vs. Japan, 27
Robot Institute of America, 19, 192
Robot Repair, 166
Rockwell International, 101, 157,
    165
    Autonetics Marine Systems
        Division of, 127–29
    HiMAT program of, 126–27
Rogers, Michael, 93
Rome, ancient:
    feedback control in, 62
    mechanical beings in, 34
rooster, mechanical, 36, 37
Rosen, Charles, 51, 57
Rountree Chocolates, 14
RPV's (remotely piloted vehicles),
    116, 123–27
    advantages of, 127
    HiMAT, 126–27
    reconnaissance functions of, 123–
    125
R2D2 ("Star Wars" robot), 46, 47,
    142
R.U.R. (Rossum's Universal Robots)
    (Čapek), 18, 44

Sacerdoti, Earl, 59
safety features, 12, 21
Sagan, Carl, 175
Salt, James, 113–14
Samuel, Arthur, 85
Sandhu, 154
Sandman (Hoffmann), 43–44
satellites:
    communications, 87
    killer, 173, 175
    repair of, 79

Scheinman, Victor, 78–79
Science Journal, 80
Scientific American, 87, 104, 107,
    162
Scout (mini-RPV), 123–25, 127
Scribe, The (Charles), 39, 40
Seiko watch factory, 98–100
sequencing relays, 154
servant robots, 138–40, 142, 145,
    151, 154
Shakey the Robot, 51–52, 53, 145
sheep shearing, use of robots for,
    14–15
Sheffield, H.M.S., 113–14, 115,
    116
    cost of, 117
Shelley, Mary, 33
Shields and Yarnell comedy team,
    54
ShowBiz Place, 148–49
show robots, 16, 133–49
Silent Running (movie), 46, 137
silicon chips, 41, 46
    CAD/CAM and, 105
    number of transistors on, 49
    vision analysis and, 68–69
Silicon Valley, 58–59
Silicon Valley (Rogers), 93
Silverberg, Robert, 46
Simon, Herbert, 80–81
Sketchpad program, 103–4
skin, artificial, 72–77
    Hillis, 74–76
    human skin compared to, 73, 76–
    77
    made from rubber rods, 72–74
    tasks performed by, 74
Sky Eye (remotely piloted vehicle),
    125, 127
slavery, human vs. mechanical, 31,
    32
Slutzky, Joel, 184
snakelike robots, 15
sonar ranging, 165
Soviet Union, 170
    "boomerang" system vs., 131–32
    cruise missiles and, 119, 120, 122

industrial robots in, 27
Lunohods of, 175, 176
robots imported by, 127
tanks in, 129–30
space-based defense system, 169–75
space robots, 169, 175–79
Space Shuttle, 101–2, 172, 177–79
Sparko (robot dog), 135, 136–37
speech recognition units, 167
spying, industrial, 58
Squirt series robots, 142, 143, 160, 164
Stanford Research Institute, 51–52, 53, 57, 145
Stanford University, 25, 26, 78, 90, 91
vision research at, 67, 68–69
Stansbarger, Donald, 97–98
Star Trek television series, 45
"Star Wars" movie series, 46, 47
Stepford Wives, The (movie), 59
stepper motors, 165
Strasbourg cathedral, mechanical rooster on, 36, 37
structured-light vision systems, 67, 68
suction cups, as substitutes for hands, 14, 22
suicidal mental patients, identification of, 90
surgery, robots and, 169, 188–89
Surveyor spacecraft, 175
Susa, Temple of, children's toys found at, 41
Sutherland, Ivan E., 103–4
switches, electronic, cost of, 20
Switzerland, watch sales of, 99
SYM-1 computer, 165

tactile senses, 25, 54–55, 58, 69–77
of Mobot I, 49–50
multi-axis force-sensor system, 70–72
need for, 69
problems with, 62
requirements of, 69–70
see also skin, artificial

Tales of Hoffman, The (Offenbach), 44
talking machines, 36–38, 145
talking robots, 133–34
tanks, robot, 116, 127, 129–31
advantages of, 130–31
teachboxes, programming with, 20
Teach Control device, 23, 24
Teachmover robot, 23–25, 157
technological change, advantages vs. disadvantages of, 30–32
teleoperators (remove manipulators), 19–20, 49–50, 137, 154
robot aircraft guided by, 123
tanks controlled by, 80
telephones, tactile, 77
telepresence, 188–89
television eyes, see eyes, television
television pictures:
"bits" of information on, 63
pixels (picture elements) of, 63–65
television sets, assembling of, 78–79
Televox (robot), 134
Teller, Edward, 131
tendon technology, 23–25
tennis instructors, robots as, 185–87
terrain matching, 120, 122
Texas, industrial robots in, 14
Texas Instruments, 14
Thatcher, Margaret, 113
therapy, 82–83
expert systems and, 89, 90
Thinking Computer, The (Raphael), 54
Thompson, Ken, 86
Three Laws of Robotics, The, 45–46
tic-tac-toe programs, 36, 83–84, 85
Tigerfish torpedos, 116–17
Time magazine, 29, 116, 170–71
To Build a Computer-Controlled Robot (Todd), 146
Tokyo Institute of Technology, 15
Tomahawk cruise missiles, 119–22
developmental problems of, 120–122

guidance of, 120
trajectory corrections of, 120
tour guides, robots as, 15
Tow wire-guided antitank missiles,
    119
Toys "R" Us, 154
traffic policemen, robots as, 15
transistors:
    advantages of, 49
    cost of, 12
    size of, 20, 21
Turing, Alan, 92
Turing test, 92, 93, 96
Turk, the (chess-playing "robot"),
    35–36
2001: A Space Odyssey (movie), 33

Ultra (robot), 144
ultrasound, robots responsive to, 25
Umetani, Yoji, 15
unemployment, 31, 32
Unicorn 1 (hobby robot), 157
Unimate, 23, 50, 54
Unimation, 14, 27, 51, 142
Union Carbide, 107–8
United States Robotics Society, 167
"Universal Automation" concept, 50
Universal Robots, 160, 164
Universal Robot Systems, 142
U.S. News & World Report, 31

vacation robots, 169, 187–88
vacuum tubes, disadvantages of, 48–
    49
Vantec, 164
Vaucanson, Jacques de, 38–39
Vaucanson Duck, 38
video games, 41, 138, 140, 166
Viking spacecraft, 175–76
Villa, Luigi, 87
Virgil of Naples, 34
vision, 56–58, 59, 62–69, 114, 147
    binocular, 26, 65–67
    computer analysis of, 68–69

range-finding, 67
revenues from, 69
structured-light, 67, 68
tactile sensors compared to, 62,
    72, 74
three-dimensional figures and,
    65–69
see also eyes, television
voice synthesizers, 166
Volkswagen, two-handed robots at,
    22
von Kempelen, Baron Wolfgang,
    35–38

warfare, defensive vs. offensive,
    117–18
War of Atonement, The (Herzog),
    118
Wasp program, 122–23
watches, assembling of, 98–100
Watt, James, 60–62
weaving looms:
    opponents of, 31
    punched holes and, 108
Weinstein, Marty, 162
Weitzenbaum, Joseph, 81–83
Westinghouse, 69, 134–37
What Computers Can't Do
    (Dreyfus), 81
Wiener, Norbert, 31
Wilde, Oscar, 32
Willie Vocalite (robot), 134, 136–37
windmills, feedback control of, 62
World War I, defensive warfare in,
    117–18
World War II:
    Blitzkrieg concept in, 118
    cruise missiles in, 119–20
    kamikaze raids in, 116
wrench sorting, 56–57, 63, 65

Yamazaki Machinery Works, 99
Yates, David, 187–88

About the Author

Tom Logsdon works as an aerospace engineer at Rockwell International, where he conducts advanced systems studies for the space-based Navstar navigation system. His previous assignments have included Project Apollo, Skylab, and the Space Shuttle. *The Robot Revolution* is his thirteenth book. His earlier ones have dealt mainly with space science and computer technology. He also writes for several magazines. Logsdon holds a master's degree in point-set topology, a highly abstract branch of mathematics. He lives on the Pacific Coast in Seal Beach, California, where he jogs (reluctantly) and plays spastic tennis.